PERMISSION

PERMISSION

HOW TO FEEL, HEAL AND THRIVE IN A CHALLENGING WORLD

Caroline Walker

Joyful
Doctor
Books

PERMISSION
How to feel, heal and thrive
in a challenging world

All the stories in this book are true, but some personal details
have been changed to protect the anonymity of others.

First published in Great Britain in 2024
by Joyful Doctor Books
a subdivision of The Joyful Doctor Ltd

ISBN (Paperback): 9781068651281
ISBN (eBook): 9781068651212

Cover design: Dr Alexandra Roberts

**Joyful
Doctor
Books**

Trigger Warning

This book contains several distressing topics including severe mental illness, suicide, physical and sexual assault, disordered eating behaviours and the deaths of babies. If you are personally affected by any of these issues, please see the 'Where to get help' pages at the back of this book or visit the 'Useful Links' page at:

www.joyfuldoctor.com

Profit Statement

The Joyful Doctor Ltd is a private company that uses its resources to improve the mental health and wellbeing of struggling doctors and other healthcare professionals. After covering costs, including author royalties, all profits from the sale of this book will help The Joyful Doctor to continue this vital work.

Praise for Permission

'Everyone should read this book, not just doctors, it might just change your life'

Dr Helen Garr
Medical Director
NHS Practitioner Health

'A must-read guide for better mental health'

Prof Dame Clare Gerada
Former President of the Royal College of GPs
& Patron of Doctors in Distress

'I read it from cover to cover in one sitting, only stopping to bat away the tears'

Dr Aicha Rais
NHS Psychiatrist

'This is SUCH a needed book, I'm so thankful you've written it'

Dr Sarah Pillinger
NHS GP

'I couldn't put it down'

Dr Rebecca Jones
The Vegan Doctor

For Joe

Contents

PERMISSION

Preface

What is it with doctors?

*"I want to be a doctor…but I'll have to be
a nurse because I'm a girl."*

Dr Caroline Walker, age 5

At the tender age of five-and-three-quarters I declared my medical ambitions to the world, AKA my mum. I know this because she wrote it down. She's one of those mums who does that sort of thing. She also sends me 'I saw this and thought of you' messages on WhatsApp about four hundred times a day.

As luck would have it, my mum was also a shoulder-padded woman of the 1980s, fighting for her rightful place in a patriarchal world. So, when faced with a culturally brainwashed five-year-old daughter who thought she could only do certain jobs because of her gender, she soon put me right. I learnt that day that I could "do anything I put my mind to". So it was, that I stepped innocently onto the medical conveyor belt.

You may be familiar with the medical conveyor belt, or one from another industry. You do OK at school, get the grades you need, go on to study and learn your chosen craft, and pop out somewhere a few years later, fresh-faced and ready to save the world.

Sadly, within just a few weeks of hitting the wards as a junior doctor, at the still quite tender age of twenty-four, I was broken. I was surrounded by death, disease, pain, and uncertainty everywhere I went, and I felt like it was all my fault. I thought that I was killing people because I didn't know what I was doing. It felt like I'd missed the day at medical school when they taught you how to be a doctor. Everyone else around me seemed to know what they were doing, and I didn't. I was waiting for the moment someone would say "Sorry, we made a mistake, you don't belong here."

I fell into bed after each fifteen-hour shift, exhausted and spent, only to dream about work all night long. Then I'd wake up and repeat the whole routine again. Day after day I came home to my soulless box of a room, my only true comfort knowing that my pager was off for a few sacred hours – a few hours in which my heart wouldn't race and my stomach wouldn't lurch into my throat at the mere sound of a bleep. I would still bristle at the sound of a passing ambulance though, joking unconvincingly that they were "playing my song".

One grey autumn morning, just a few weeks into my first job as a junior doctor, I was slumped at a nursing station looking up blood results for what felt like the hundredth time that day. Suddenly, as if from nowhere, a handsome cardiology registrar popped up in front of me.

"Hi, how are you doing?" he asked in a light-hearted and friendly way.

Without thinking I replied, in a mockingly chipper tone: "I'm thinking of resigning thanks, how are you?"

There was a long awkward pause.

We looked at each other and both silently acknowledged two things. Firstly, something wasn't right – I was clearly *not* OK. Secondly, we were both British and doctors, and there was no way that we were going to talk about our feelings, especially at work.

Instead, we did what any good British doctors would do – we awkwardly laughed it off. He told me about a patient on the ward who he'd just reviewed, and then he went on his way. I didn't give it another thought. I was, after all, too busy worrying that I was killing people and trying to cover up my paralysing fear and ineptitude at every turn.

Later that day, on The Ward Round That Never Ended, that same cardiology registrar walked up to me again and passed me a little pink piece of paper. I recognised it immediately. It was a cardiology request form.

"That's odd" I thought to myself. "Why would a cardiologist be asking me to do a cardiology investigation? Surely it should be the other way around?"

"It's OK," he said quietly. "Don't read this now. Read it later when you get home." And off he went.

Slightly puzzled and intrigued, I put the little pink note

in my pocket and went on with my day.

Later that night when I got home, exhausted after yet another relentless shift, I found the forgotten note in my pocket and read it.

I still have that little hand-written note twenty years later. It's one of the most compassionate and courageous letters I've ever received. He wrote that, at the risk of embarrassing himself, he wanted to reach out to me. He'd sensed that something wasn't right when we'd spoken earlier.

He went on to say, in a typically British understated way, that being a junior doctor is "...in many ways quite tough... and every now and again one hears such sad stories of colleagues (of all ages and seniorities) who are struggling, who feel unsupported (who are unsupported) and who consequently go on to such things as breakdowns, overdoses and even suicide attempts."

He said that he trusted that I would think carefully about my options and would make the right decision for me, and that if he could help me in any way, I could come along and have a cup of tea and a chat with him at any time.

Then came the postscript – one that I will never forget.

"Background: In 1999 a very close friend of our family, a GP Registrar, died by suicide, leaving behind his wife and three children. No one even guessed he was having problems."

"No one even guessed he was having problems."

Those words clattered around my brain on repeat, for

several minutes, refusing to settle.

That was the moment I realised just how much we can struggle as doctors, how hard we can find it to look after ourselves, and how difficult it can be to get help when we need it the most.

Looking back, it was also the first time I realised what really helps a doctor who's struggling in their darkest moments. It's not always the big interventions that cost a lot of money or take a lot of time. It's often simple moments of human kindness such as this one: one person noticing that their fellow human being is struggling and reaching out to offer them support, a cup of tea or a listening ear.

These small acts of compassion and humanity can literally save someone's life. I have no doubt that little pink note saved *my* life that day.

I didn't realise it at the time, but I was deeply depressed and having suicidal thoughts. Left alone in my own desperate and dark head, things could have ended very differently for me that day. As they did for Dr Rose Polge, a junior doctor undertaking her first year on the wards at that same hospital twelve years later.

On February 12, 2016, Rose uncharacteristically left the hospital part way through her shift. Those close to her knew she'd been struggling and rapidly raised the alarm. Her car was found close to the sea, with a handwritten note to her friends and family in the glove compartment.

Despite widespread efforts and great endeavours by Search and Rescue teams, after a couple of weeks the search for Rose was called off. Sadly, two months later, her body was found at sea, fifty miles along the coast.

As I write this book it's eight years since Rose died, and approximately one doctor is dying by suicide every ten days in the UK.[1] Female doctors in particular are nearly twice as likely to die by suicide than the general population.[2] If we broaden out to look at all NHS staff, since 2011, over 2,500 healthcare workers have died by suicide – that's the equivalent of four every week.[3]

NHS Practitioner Health (NPH) – a confidential service for doctors and dentists with mental health conditions – currently receives around 550 to 650 self-referrals a month. And on September 17th 2024, NPH along with the charity Doctors in Distress, held the UK's first annual National Suicide Memorial Day for Health and Care Workers.[4]

This is clearly not just about me, and it is not just about Rose. There's something much bigger going on for healthcare workers and their mental health. And something needs to change.

The day that kind cardiology registrar reached out to me in 2004 was the tentative beginning of my journey of recovery as a doctor. Since that day I've had many dark moments and many wonderful moments too, some of which you'll read about in the pages of this book. From that moment though, the seeds of hope were sown. I realised I wasn't alone in feeling the way I did. I could glimpse that there *might* be a way to get better.

That little pink note gave me permission to stop pretending I was OK. It gave me permission to *not* be OK, and to talk about it honestly and openly with another person. That note gave me permission to be who I was; to be a human being and a doctor at the same time.

That day was also the beginning of my love affair with the world of mental health and doctors' wellbeing. I went on to train as a psychiatrist and psychotherapist in the NHS, taking a couple of career breaks along the way to branch out into such diverse fields as professional decluttering and organising, paper crafting and coaching. Over the past decade or so, I have come to focus solely on the wellbeing of doctors, inventing my own title of Doctors' Wellbeing Specialist which has inspired others to do the same.

I currently look after a caseload of doctors for NHS Practitioner Health, and in 2017 I founded The Joyful Doctor – an organisation dedicated to improving the wellbeing of doctors through community, coaching and creativity. Since we started, we've helped thousands of doctors to look after themselves through individual and group coaching, workshops, talks, online courses, podcast episodes and more. With Joyful Doctor Books we hope to help many more with the healing power of doctors' words.

I have always wanted to write a book about the mental health and wellbeing of doctors – and this is it. What you're about to read is a collection of my experiences, both personal and professional, since that day my life was saved as a junior doctor. It is a selection of my own and my doctor-patients' stories, meaningful moments, top tips and ideas, that have helped me and countless others to feel, heal and thrive in this challenging world.

This book is primarily about doctors, and is written by a doctor, but you don't have to be a doctor to read it. If you're someone who cares for other people but struggles to care for yourself, this book will help you. Whoever you are, I hope it will help you in your moments of need when you're struggling the most, and in your moments of feeling better when you have more capacity to thrive. I hope it will inspire you, uplift you, comfort you, and bring you hope that there's always a way to get through tough times.

If you're looking for a lot of scientific theories and heavily referenced words about mental health, this book is not for you. If, on the other hand, you'd like to read a mixture of stories and ideas about how to maintain good mental health and live a more joyful life as a caring person, please read on. Some chapters will offer practical ideas and solutions; others will offer personal stories and examples of how *permission* could be useful in your day-to-day life, as it has been in mine.

"Why *permission*?" you may be wondering. Read on and you will discover more on this in the next chapter. Hopefully you'll find each chapter of this book thought-provoking and helpful, if not now, then maybe in the future, or for someone else you know. If you have any thoughts on any topics in this book, or any topics you wish I'd covered, please email me and my team at *books@joyfuldoctor.com*. You never know, your thoughts may appear in print one day and help others too.

A quick disclaimer: the opinions I express in this book are just that – opinions. Any professional who tells you they're entirely objective in their work is lying to both you and themselves. My opinions are drawn from years of academic study, decades of personal and professional experience, and more than a little pinch of intuition, faith and personal bias. While I believe in what I've written right now, I may change my mind over time, and I may be proved wrong. Like many people, I hold contradictory views about certain things. When it comes to mental health and wellbeing, I know I hold different opinions to some of my most respected colleagues and peers, and that's exactly how it should be.

I'm so happy that you've stayed with me to read this far. I hope that my words will help and inspire you. Please take what you like and leave the rest.

Prologue

Why Permission?

"I didn't have to be good. I just had to give it a go."

Jessi Tucker
1980-2022
Doctor, Environmentalist, Poet, Friend

"Don't run in the road." "Eat your greens." "Speak up." "Shut up." As children we learn quickly what we *are* and *are not* supposed to do. As we grow up, we listen to those around us and watch what they do, consciously and unconsciously learning how we should and shouldn't behave in the world. Without realising it, we gather a long list of *permissions* for how to live our lives. "Don't cry." "Say please and thank you." "Don't do drugs." "Go to medical school." Sometimes the rules are obvious and sometimes they're not.

Think about it for a moment. What list of *permissions* do you live your life by? Do you have permission to eat what you want, wear what you want and say what you want? Do you have permission to move your body how you want to and do a job you want to do? Can you spend time with the people you love? Can you say out loud what you're really thinking? Can you show up in the world as you truly are?

Where do these permissions come from? Who gave you these permissions in the first place? Are you looking for permission from others, or are you able to give yourself the permission you need right now?

In my years of working with doctors to improve their mental health I've noticed one pervasive theme: *a lack of permission.*

Doctors, like most human beings, tend to look to others for the permission they need. Doctors watch and learn from other doctors. If one doctor takes a break away from their computer at lunchtime it allows another doctor to do the same. If one doctor leaves work on time, says no to a task or speaks up when something isn't right, then more will follow suit. If one doctor shares openly about their struggles with anxiety, neurodiversity or burnout, more will start to share their stories too.

So, what does a doctor do when all the other doctors around them are skipping meals, staying late at work and pushing themselves to breaking point? They do the same. In this environment, how does a doctor get the permission they so desperately need to take care of themselves? The answer is simple, but not necessarily easy. Each doctor must *give themselves* permission to do what they need to do. Just as I gave myself permission to write this book and, thankfully, you have given yourself permission to read it, we must each find a way to give ourselves permission.

Whether you're a doctor or not, I hope you can give yourself permission to look after yourself and put yourself first in your own life. If you're worried about the impact this will have on others or feel a sense of guilt for putting yourself first, let me assure you that looking after yourself is far from a selfish act. When you're well and your needs are being met, you can have a much greater positive impact on the lives of others. Put simply: if you take care of yourself, you can help others more. I call it 'self-care for unselfish reasons' and I hope it catches on.

I invite you to start by giving yourself permission to read this book however you want to. Dip in and out of it or devour it from cover to cover. Try out some of the ideas for yourself or pooh-pooh them as pseudo-scientific nonsense. Put it down and never open it again or finish it in one sitting and buy copies for all your friends. Whatever you do, consciously *choose* to do it.

Give yourself permission.

1

Permission to be ill

"We all get sick."

Eve Ensler

"Doctors shouldn't take sick leave. It's selfish. They should put their patients' needs first."

My jaw dropped.

Did my consultant *really* just say that?

The Human Resources (HR) manager across from me looked equally shocked and bewildered. Neither of us knew what to say.

We'd just started a sickness review meeting triggered by some sick leave I'd taken in recent weeks, and this was my consultant's opening gambit – that doctors simply shouldn't take sick leave. Ever.

I wish someone had taken a snapshot of my face in that moment. It would have shown a baffling mix of confusion, disbelief and bemusement. It may have also shown a flicker of fear, shame and powerlessness as my brain battled to compute what this meant for my job. The power differential was not in my favour and it immediately put me on the back foot, trying not to say or do anything that could make the situation worse.

You might be wondering how much sick leave I'd taken to provoke this damning statement from my consultant. The answer is three days.

In the preceding six-month period, I'd taken one day off sick for a urinary tract infection, during which I spent most of the time sitting on a toilet, peeing fire. I'd taken one day off for a migraine, during which time I lay in a pitch-black room for hours, feeling as if the sun was piercing through my left eye socket and incinerating my brain. Finally, I'd taken one day off after a week of annual leave, which I'd spent sleeping upright on the sofa, pumped full of antibiotics and steroids for pneumonia. I wanted to wait until I was well enough to safely walk between the hospital buildings at work, without fainting or coughing up a lung, before I returned to work.

These three separate instances of sick leave, all perfectly legitimate and treated appropriately by my own GP, occurred within a six-month period. This triggered our trust's formal sickness policy, and I was therefore 'invited' to a formal sickness review meeting with my line manager (my consultant) and a representative from HR. Having taken several periods of sick leave earlier in my career for my mental health and recurrent tonsillitis, I was familiar with these meetings. I'd learnt that I didn't need to fear them - they were designed to support me.

This was different to the first such letter I'd received years earlier. The officious wording of which made me think I was being summoned to defend myself in court for crimes against humanity. I still regularly see these letters striking fear into the hearts of unsuspecting doctors when their only 'crime' is to follow medical advice and take time off sick when they are ill. In fact, I now routinely warn my doctor-patients to expect these letters and try to reassure them that they are simply a routine HR tool designed to facilitate and demonstrate due process.

By the time this latest invitation had arrived, I was an old hand and was able to reassure myself that this meeting was just a formality. This particular 'frequent episodes of sick leave' protocol existed to pick up those who might be struggling, who needed to take longer off or required more support in the workplace. It was also designed to deter those who might be abusing the system by taking random days off sick just for the fun of it. Both of these reasons I could get on board with.

So when we kicked off the meeting, I was prepared for a quick check-in and something apologetic in the way of an opening bid. Something along the lines of: "Sorry about this. It's just protocol. How are you? I hope you're doing OK. Do you have all the support you need? Is there anything else we can do to support you?" Instead, I was hit with the deeply stigmatising and sharply barbed "Doctors shouldn't take sick leave" and my brain didn't know what to do with it.

Since that day I've recounted those consultant's words many times, as a clear example of the stigma around doctors' ill health that has existed in the medical profession for centuries. I've tried many times to come up with a sensible, assertive, even witty response that I could have shot back in that moment, but I'm no Oscar Wilde. I'm just a human being, trying to be a good doctor and manage my normal health issues at the same time.

Thankfully these archaic attitudes are starting to shift. However, there are many things I want to say in response to any health-shaming culture that does still exist in medicine today.

I want to say:

Of course doctors get sick. It's ridiculous to think we don't.

I want to say:

Be logical. Sick people aren't the best people to be looking after other sick people.

I want to say:

A doctor must be well if they're going to be safe. Sometimes, when they're not well, it's not safe for them to be working.

I want to say:

Doctors who take sick leave *are* putting their patients first. They're looking after themselves in line with their 'modern-day Hippocratic oath', the Declaration of Geneva.[5] It's their *duty* to care for themselves, to ensure they don't work when unwell, and to do no harm.

I want to say:

We should be encouraging doctors to take more sick leave – not discouraging it. Not only should doctors take sick leave, but they should take it sooner than they do and stay off for longer than they think they should.

Perhaps most importantly of all, I want to say this:

Doctors are human beings, and they deserve to take sick leave when they are sick. Doctors have a right to be cared for and relieved of the burdens of work when they're unwell, just like anyone else.

Doctors are often prevented from looking after themselves when they're sick by a toxic mix of institutionalised discrimination, poor role-modelling and internalised fear and shame. They are specifically discouraged from doing what they're trained to help others to do – look after their health.

Most doctors have been touched by the pervasive culture of presenteeism and health-shaming in medicine at some point in their careers. General Practitioners (GPs) regularly get complaints from their patients for not being available to see them – despite their patients knowing that they were off sick. Doctors of all specialties and seniorities have been asked by peers and line managers to consider if they are 'resilient enough' to keep doing their job, after experiencing periods of relatively common ill health and recovery.

Stigma and shame pervade the healthcare environment, invisibly, silently, and they can kill. Struggling doctors who go on to die by suicide often verbalise the wounds of this shaming in the weeks before their death. They allude to their sense of failure, and rejection from a profession that's meant to care for human beings, but didn't care enough for them.

I work with doctors every day who live in fear of what their colleagues will think if they take time off sick. Most of them have never had anything said to them directly like I have, but they still carry a palpable sense of existential threat. When they try to put it into words it often manifests as a concern that they'll be 'talked about' or 'thought less of' somehow by their colleagues.

Sometimes doctors will have experienced direct evidence of this from other doctors; for example, overhearing a colleague's comment such as: "Oh they're off sick again, are they?" or "What is it this time?" Sometimes it's more indirect, for example, "Wouldn't it be nice if we could all take a day off?" or "Great, that leaves even more work for the rest of us."

I like to think that the people uttering these stigmatising micro-aggressions don't realise the impact of the beliefs embedded within them. I also hope that they don't become victims of their own internalised judgements one day when *they* become unwell and need some time off.

The shame and stigma within medicine isn't the only challenge doctors face when they become patients. Doctors get just as many physical and mental illnesses as other people – sometimes more. They also have the added advantages and disadvantages of being a doctor and patient at the same time.

Doctors, like anyone, can veer wildly between hypochondriacal and totally dismissive when faced with their own signs and symptoms of possible illness. No matter how much medical training or experience a doctor has, they can still obsess that their headache is a brain tumour or brush off their chest pain as 'just a twinge'.

Doctors healing rare and frightening conditions in their patients can understandably overestimate the risk when they or their loved ones experience similar symptoms. Conversely, blunted by years of managing life and death crises, they can easily underplay their own and their colleagues' health concerns.

Doctors can sometimes benefit from their own medical knowledge and experience of navigating the healthcare system, but they can also face many obstacles to receiving the care and treatment they need. They often feel pressure to manage their symptoms and signs on their own. They fear recrimination for showing any signs of 'weakness'.

They worry about the impact on their appraisals and their career progression. They fear for their reputation and standing in their local and wider medical communities, and in the public eye should they be seen to have 'something wrong with them'. They fear for their financial security. They worry about confidentiality and getting into trouble with their regulatory body. The list goes on and on as they stay trapped in an endless cycle of fear and shame.

When doctors do get sick, they generally tend to delay taking sick leave as long as possible and return to work as soon as they can. There are numerous stories in circulation of doctors narrowly averting paralysis or even death because they delayed seeking appropriate medical care for themselves. These stories are often dismissed as apocryphal, but I have treated several such doctors myself over the years.

The question of when a doctor should return to work after a period of ill health is also complicated by many unhelpful cultural beliefs. In my experience, most doctors, including myself, will instinctively want to return to work the moment they think they're better. Unfortunately, we tend to draw this line far too soon.

We may have been in bed with the flu for five days, but the first time we manage to walk downstairs and consume a meal sitting at a table is often the moment we start planning our return to world domination. Never mind that we spend the next five hours comatose on the sofa in response to the massive exertion of eating a simple meal.

Doctors can often be found masochistically coughing, spluttering and sneezing their way through patient lists, popping painkillers between appointments and repeatedly exclaiming "I'm fine thanks" to all who ask. Or found sobbing in a bathroom cubicle because they came back to work too soon after a period of sick leave.

Any reprieve doctors experienced as COVID hit, when good self-care was mandated and normalised for a while, disappeared with the return to 'business as usual'. It's sad how quickly the medical profession has forgotten the importance of putting our own health first, not infecting our colleagues or patients, and giving ourselves adequate time to heal.

At the other end of the spectrum, doctors can also be encouraged to stay off work for too long by unhelpful comments from colleagues. For example: "Wait until you're *one hundred percent* better to come back to work." In practice, doctors often need to return before they are one hundred percent better, to complete their recovery in the work environment.

Deciding the best point of return to work, for a doctor on sick leave, is a delicate art. It takes skill and experience to judge the balance between the need to complete their rehabilitation in the work environment and the resilience they will need to do an unpredictable and risky job safely.

You may be a fan of percentages and want a better guiding principle than 'one hundred percent better' before returning to work. Please bear in mind that no such percentage exists, and it will vary massively depending on the individual, the condition, and the work environment. In my own practice, I often plump for a doctor being between sixty and eighty percent better before recommending they return to work.

There are also many doctors, protected by the Equality Act 2010, with semi-permanent or permanent disabilities who may require reasonable adjustments to be made in the workplace before returning.[6] These can include such recommendations as altered hours, amended duties or a phased return; lasting anywhere from one week to many months or more.

It's important to keep all this in mind when you're welcoming a colleague back from sick leave. Don't expect them to be 'one hundred percent' or to 'hit the ground running'. Depending on the circumstances, some doctors can take anywhere from several months up to a year or longer to get back to a stable level of performance after a period of prolonged absence.

It is important to give yourself and your colleagues permission to be ill. Permission to take time off sick, time to get better, and to have good and bad days when you return to work. Permission to slow down or extend a period of sickness absence or phased return as needed. And permission to go off sick again if you need to. After all, most of us will get sick more than once in our working lifetime.

2

Permission to feel safe

*"When we feel safe enough to expose our shadows,
that's when we become free."*

Gabrielle Bernstein

We all need to feel safe. Yet human life is full of threat and danger. So where do we get our sense of safety from?

If we're lucky, our early life experiences are predictable, nurturing, and devoid of excessive trauma. They allow us to develop a sense of safety in a secure environment, surrounded and supported by our early caregivers. Sadly, for many of us, this is not the case. Due to the conscious and unconscious actions of others, and situations beyond our control, many of us are left with an inadequate sense of safety going into adulthood.

The good news is that it's never too late to learn how to feel safe. A sense of safety in the world can be instilled, built upon and nurtured at any stage of life. Some people find safety in a long-term stable relationship with another person, a job or even a building. Others find safety internally by using safe-place visualisations or grounding techniques. Others need professional help and treatment, as I did, to feel safe again in the world. You may find a sense of safety in the pages of this book; I hope you do. Whatever works for you, when it comes to feeling safe, is OK.

We need to feel safe to do almost anything else in our lives in a healthy way. To breathe, eat, rest, sleep, talk, move, have sex and think clearly, we need to feel safe. We need to feel psychologically safe if we want to be honest with ourselves and others, courageously face our emotions and meet our mental health needs.

Ask yourself this: "How safe do I feel right now?"

If the answer that comes back makes you realise you could feel safer, then try one of the following three strategies to boost your sense of safety in this moment: Remember, Connect or Ground.

Remember

Remember a time and place when you felt completely safe. Immerse yourself in that memory: what you felt, what you could see, hear, smell and touch, and what you were thinking. Continue reliving that memory until you start to feel safer in your body right now.

Connect

Connect with another person that you feel safe around –

by text, phone or in person. Or bring an image of that person to mind. Imagine being with them until you start to feel safer in this moment now.

Ground

Ground yourself in the present moment by describing three things in detail that you can see, hear and touch right now. Slowly describe each of these three things in as much detail as you can before moving onto the next.

For example, right now as I write this sentence, I can see a mug of tea on the table next to me. It is a plain white ceramic mug that tapers from a wide round top to a narrower round bottom. The handle is pointing towards me, and the mug is approximately two thirds full with a dark watery liquid. There is a slight tide mark above the level of the liquid, as if the mug has been sitting for a while and the liquid has started to evaporate. Which reminds me that I should probably take a sip of my tea before it goes cold!

Describing each of the three things you can see, hear and touch right now in such detail, will help to bring you out of your past or future worries and into a calmer awareness of the present moment.

If any of these strategies have been helpful for you, you might want to mark this page to come back to, to help you in moments when you feel unsettled or unsafe. For example, if any chapters in this book stir up difficult memories or feelings for you, you can return to this page at any time and anchor yourself in a feeling of safety.

Give yourself permission to feel safe.

Note: It is common for human beings to need professional help to feel safe, particularly those of us who have experienced traumatic events. Doctors, by the nature of their work, often fall into this category. The good news is that trauma is treatable, so please reach out for help if you think you might need it. Check out chapter 18 of this book 'Permission to feel traumatised', the pages on 'Where to get help' at the end of this book or visit our 'Useful Links' page at *www.joyfuldoctor.com*.

3

Permission to fall

"All the great things are simple, and many can be expressed in a single word: freedom, honour, justice, duty, mercy... hope."

Winston Churchill

By my late twenties, I had experienced a blip or two with my mental health. My heart had been broken a couple of times, and I'd survived a major 'breakdown' and at least one episode of severe depression. By the autumn of 2008 I'd met the man I was going to marry, and I was training to be a psychiatrist in the East of England.

One weekend I was driving to do an on-call shift at the hospital where I worked. I felt awful and I didn't know why. On my journey, driving across the fens of East Anglia, my head was desperately searching for any excuse I could use to call in sick and go home.

Unfortunately, no excuse came and my car kept driving forwards. When I eventually arrived at work, I made my way to the handover room and waited for the doctor from the night shift to join me. I felt fearful and on edge, and I still couldn't put my finger on why.

A few moments later the night shift doctor came into the room. She smiled at me warmly and went to hand me the on-call bleep. In that moment the world stopped still. My movements went into slow motion. I saw my hand reaching out to take the bleep from hers and then it stopped. I felt my legs give way, and my whole body was overtaken by an involuntary sob as I fell to the floor.

I couldn't do it anymore.

I'm so grateful to that amazing doctor (you know who you are) for what she did next. She didn't hesitate for a second. Within moments she had sat me down, comforted me and given me a cup of tea. She was talking to me so kindly, telling me she'd called a colleague to come in and cover my shift that day. Her kind and comforting words washed over me in a misty haze as my brain struggled to compute what was happening.

She told me she'd phoned my partner and asked him to come and pick me up because I was in no fit state to drive. Then, despite being exhausted from her night shift, she stayed with me until my partner arrived, continuing to tell me repeatedly that it was all going to be OK.

An hour later my partner walked in and scooped me up into his arms. He thanked the night shift doctor and started to walk me outside to take me home. As we walked across the car park towards his car, the world seemed slow and hazy around me.

"What about *my* car? How will I get it home? What's happening? I... I don't understand."

"It's OK," he replied softly. "I'll come back with you another day to get your car. It will be OK."

I don't know if he really believed what he was saying. He seemed as confused as I was by what was going on.

As he drove me home, back across the misty fens, I stared out of the window in a daze. A stretch of whitewashed wall flashed beside me at the side of the road. I realised that I had been driving past that stretch of wall every day for the last few weeks, thinking about driving my car into it, hoping to die.

Today it was different.

"That's not normal," I thought to myself. "That's a suicidal thought."

My brain slowly took this in.

My thoughts continued: "I'm a psychiatrist, and I'm having suicidal thoughts. That's not normal. I must be depressed."

When we got home to our two-bedroom flat, I sat bewildered on the sofa, feeling like an alien that had landed in a strange new world. The world as I knew it had collapsed around me. I couldn't think straight and I didn't understand what was happening. I just kept thinking: "That's it. I'll never be able to work as again. How can I ever go back? What will my colleagues think of me? What will I tell my family? My life is over."

Without my knowing, the doctor from the night shift

had helped me in one final way that day. She'd called one of our local consultants who she knew would be kind, and asked her to give me a call later that day. I was still sitting on my sofa staring into space when the phone rang.

The consultant's voice was so gentle and reassuring. Her words drifted over me in a soothing haze. She said, "Caroline – burnout is a serious thing. It will be OK. You will take some time off, go to see Occupational Health, get some help and come back when you are ready. It will be OK."

"*It will be OK.*"

Those words perfused my brain like a warm beam of sunshine on a cloudy day. I was still scared and confused, but a senior colleague, someone I trusted, had reassured me I was going to be OK. I could still be a doctor. I wasn't going to lose my job. I didn't have to keep going, pretending everything was all right. There was a path out of this nightmare and, if I accepted the support on offer, I would get better and I would be OK.

Looking back now, I realise those four little words, "It will be OK", were another great example of how a simple, kind and compassionate intervention could save a struggling doctor's life. I had no hope of my own that day, but I believed in her reassurances. Once again, the kind words of a colleague, like those in the little pink note four years earlier, had saved my life.

The Occupational Health doctor I saw a few days later immediately won me over with his gentle honesty and quotes from Blackadder. He helped me to see that I wasn't just "a bit stressed" as I'd put it to him. I was depressed, and quite severely depressed at that. But I would still be OK. I wouldn't "get back to work tomorrow", as I kept telling myself, but I *would* get back to work in time and I would still be an excellent doctor.

I did return to work, after just one month. One month! I look back now and think how crazy that was. Why didn't I give myself more time? But I couldn't give myself permission to do that. I was so self-critical and wrapped up in my identity as a doctor, that all I could do was focus on getting back to work as soon as humanly possible. It felt deeply wrong to take any time off. At that time, being a doctor wasn't just what I did for a job, it was who I believed I was as a person.

Thankfully, my Occupational Health doctor softened my speedy plans to return to work by suggesting a phased return over a few weeks. He said, "On that first day back, just walk in the front door. That's all you need to do. Just walk in and sit down." This sounded crazy to me. If I wasn't running at a hundred miles an hour what use could I be as a doctor? How could I possibly keep up? But, of course, he was right.

That first day back was, far and away, the hardest day of my career up to that point. His wise words were ringing in my ears as I walked at a snail's pace to the front door of the hospital. "Just walk in the front door. That's all you need to do. Just walk in and sit down." Wise words indeed – words I have repeated many times to my own doctor-patients. "Just walk through the door and sit down. That's all you need to do. It will be OK."

Within a few months of returning to work, I was back to working my normal shift patterns again, including night shifts. Unfortunately, life still had some nasty surprises in store for me and it was many more months before I began to feel like my normal self. My return to health was a bumpy ride with many moments of despair and joy.

It was also the beginning of a new phase of life – a phase where I gave myself permission to be more honest with myself and others about how I was feeling. I started to show more of myself, not just my doctor-self, to those around me, including my colleagues, friends, family and my first ever therapist.

As I shared my true self with others they reciprocated in kind. I recall one of my colleagues telling me about a time when he was depressed as a young doctor. He told me that he used to measure his bad days by how many times he thought about shooting himself in the head. If he didn't have that thought it was a good day.

Overall, it is a time I look back on with immense pride. I simply put one foot in front of the other and made it through each day, one day at a time. I slowly learnt how to be in the world again after everything in that world had been turned upside down. I survived.

In time I drew closer to my friends, loved ones and colleagues, and I got to know myself better too. This permission to be the 'real me', and to honestly connect with those closest to me, continues to enrich my life beyond measure to this day.

I now know I have permission to fall, and to keep falling, for as long as I need to. And I have permission to get back up, with the help of trusted others, when I'm ready.

4

Permission to break

"Every time we think we have measured our capacity to meet a challenge, we look up and we're reminded that that capacity may well be limitless."

President Josiah Bartlett
in *The West Wing* by Aaron Sorkin

In the months after I returned to work, I raised my eyes to meet the world again. My mood continued to lift and I noticed that life was blooming. It was early March, spring had arrived and there was a sense of possibility in the air. Daffodils had opened and ducklings were huddled by the river in Ely where I lived. Everywhere I looked there was new life, new beginnings and new hope.

Then came along the worst week of my life.

At the end of my first night shift back after sick leave, one of the patients I had been caring for overnight nearly died by suicide. She was a young woman tormented by severe depression and she deliberately stepped in front of a passing car outside the hospital. I was walking out of the hospital entrance, heading to my car to go home, when I saw her body lying in the gutter with a passer-by kneeling by her side. She was seizing and foaming at the mouth. She had an obvious traumatic brain injury and, within minutes, had stopped breathing.

More and more first responders came to help and we safely transferred her to the hospital's Emergency Department. We valiantly fought to save her life whilst we waited for the Air Ambulance to transport her to a nearby specialist unit for further life-saving treatment. By some miracle she survived, but the whole incident was deeply traumatic for everyone involved, including me.

The day after this awful event occurred, I suffered my first ever stress-induced migraine at work. No surprise there, given what had happened the day before. But unfortunately my symptoms were atypical, so I spent several hours in the Emergency Department as a patient myself, while they tried to rule out a possible brain tumour or brain haemorrhage (something my grandmother had died from at an early age).

Eventually I was booked in to have an urgent brain scan later that week and released. I walked back to my ward to collect my bag and go home. When I got there, I looked at my phone and saw that I had twelve missed calls from my mum.

You know that feeling when your phone rings in the middle of the night, or when someone says they *need to speak to you*? I immediately had that feeling, and I couldn't have imagined what I was about to hear in my worst nightmares.

I'd never heard my mum's voice like it. A strange mix of shock, strain and distance. It was clear that something very bad had happened and that she was struggling to say the words aloud.

Eventually the words came.

My brother Brad and his wife had been expecting a baby any day, and my sister-in-law had gone into labour. They'd driven straight to the hospital, but when the nurse went to attach the foetal monitor they couldn't find the baby's heartbeat. They scanned her abdomen and confirmed that their baby had died. My sister-in-law had to deliver their beautiful, perfect, baby boy Joe, at full-term, dead. He was stillborn.

My heart broke.

I hung up the phone and sat in silence. I couldn't think. My head was still pounding from the possible brain tumour / haemorrhage / atypical migraine. I couldn't make sense of what I'd just heard. It couldn't be true. They must have got it wrong. How could one of my severely ill patients have a miraculous escape from death one day, and my perfectly healthy baby nephew be dead the next?

In the next moment I knew I had to be with my brother and his wife. I immediately phoned my other brother, Tom, and we both went, as fast as we could, to be by their sides.

It was honestly one of worst weeks of my life. One of those 'life will never be the same again' weeks. How could anything be the same after that?

Many years have now passed since Joe died, but there are times when it feels like yesterday. In those moments my heart sinks deep into my stomach and I think of what my brother and his wife must have gone through, and what they must still go through when they think of their son. In rare and fleeting moments, I dare to imagine losing my own children and I can't breathe. There can surely be no pain worse for a parent than losing a child.

It's hard to put into words the profound impact that losing Joe had on all our lives. When I think of him I immediately remember what's most important to me: the people I love, my family, doing something meaningful with my life. Thinking of Joe helps me to conquer any fear. I think about how he never had the chance to be afraid, and I remember how lucky I am to be able to fear.

When I set up The Joyful Doctor, to help doctors to look after themselves, I was so scared of 'getting it wrong'. Thinking about Joe helped me realise that even if my worst fears did come true, it would never be as bad as losing him. As I write this book, I'm filled with anxious thoughts about the criticism I might receive from those who read it. Thinking of Joe helps me to stay courageous in the face of that vulnerability and to keep writing.

It was hard to come back from losing Joe. Life lost its meaning for all of us for a while. It was difficult to get up and go back to work and act as if everything was normal, because it wasn't.

I'd only just clawed my way back from the grips of depression before Joe died. In the space of two days, I'd seen one of my patients nearly die from suicide, been told I might have a brain tumour, and suffered the profound personal loss of a much-loved and longed-for nephew. I found it very hard to come back to work after that. I felt I couldn't do it anymore. I'd lost the will to keep trying and I felt I wasn't cut out to be a doctor. I was just going through the motions and I knew I couldn't keep going.

I asked to meet with the kind consultant who'd called me the day I went off sick, and I told her I wanted to resign. She paused, and then she gave me the greatest gift she could have given me in that moment: *permission*.

I thought I only had *one* option: to accept that I couldn't be a doctor and a human being at the same time; that I had to leave medicine behind me for good. She suggested I *could* do that, or I could take a career break for a while instead and keep my options open. In that moment, without me realising it, she gave me permission *to take a break*.

I listened to her advice and took a career break from medicine for nearly two years. A few years later, when I was again uncertain of my future career path, I took another helpful career break from my senior training years. Both breaks ultimately helped me to stay working in medicine, as a doctor, for many more years to come. I owe that all to her – for helping me to see that there's always more than one choice when we feel stuck and in need of a change. We always have permission to take a break, whether it's a five-minute tea break, a month of sick leave or a year-long sabbatical, it's all OK.

When I took that first career break, I honestly thought I'd never go back to being a doctor again. I thought I was leaving medicine for good. But it gave me a safety net – the option to return if I wanted to. It gave me permission, not only to be a little broken for a while, but to *take a break* for as long as I needed.

.

5

Permission to worry

"I have known a great many troubles,
but most of them never happened."

Mark Twain

Worry is normal. We all worry. It's common to worry about all sorts of things: our loved ones, our health, our future. As human beings we also spend a lot of time worrying about worry. Sometimes worry helps us – prompting us to take useful action or solve a problem. At other times, worry is more problematic; for example, when it takes on too much significance or makes our day-to-day existence a misery.

If you're someone who struggles with worry, the first thing you could try is normalising it. Say something like: "It's OK. It's normal to worry." Sometimes, just this simple act of compassionate acceptance is enough to help you get on with your day. If this doesn't ease your worry, I recommend trying something called The Tiger Test.

The Tiger Test

Imagine for a moment that a tiger is running towards you and is about to eat you. I think you would agree that this is a *right now*, real-life worry. We call this kind of worry a 'tiger worry'. If a tiger is about to eat you, it's entirely sensible to be worried and you need to do something about it.

When faced with a worry in everyday life however, it's rarely a 'tiger' that is worrying you.

For example, if I'm worried about what you'll think of this book, I might sit for hours worrying and not writing a single word on the page. If, on the other hand, I can catch myself worrying about this and ask myself "Is this a tiger worry?" the answer will be "No". What you think about this book is not going to kill me, and is not happening right now as I write this sentence. Immediately I start to feel more relaxed and I can carry on writing.

When you catch yourself worrying about something, ask yourself: "Is this a tiger worry?" In other words: "Is this a *right now*, real-life worry?"

If the answer is "Yes", then take appropriate action immediately.

If the answer is "No", then realising it's not a tiger worry may be enough for you to put the worry to one side and carry on with your day.

What about non-tiger worries?

If you find yourself bothered by 'non-tiger' worries, try one of these simple worry-management techniques:

Worry Bin

Imagine taking the worry from your head, screwing it up into a ball and throwing it in the 'worry bin'. Or literally write the worry down and throw it in a real bin.

When I do the latter, I like to imagine the bin is on the other side of a massive sports stadium packed full of fans, and when I make the impossible shot the crowd goes wild! If we're going to spend a lot of time worrying as human beings, why not have some fun with it?

Worry Time/ Worry List

Write your worries down and put them aside for an allocated 'Worry Time'. Set a time aside in your diary (twenty minutes or so) when you'll actively think about them.

I call this 'Joyful Worry Time' because of how quickly it helps me to worry less at other times. It doesn't stop you worrying completely, but when you do worry you can say to yourself: "OK, I'll think about that at my next Worry Time."

I know one doctor who calls it 'Winning Time' because it helps her feel she is winning at life. Many people who use this technique also find that when they get to their allotted worry time, they aren't worried anymore. Bonus! Why not give it a try?

Make a Plan

Make a plan to do something about your worry, taking appropriate action in a reasonable timeframe. For example, if you're worried about your friend's mental health, maybe set a reminder to message them later today to check how they are.

Visualise

Use a visualisation technique to let go of your worries. For example: imagine you're standing next to a beautiful stream. Imagine placing each of your worries on a separate leaf, and then watching them gently float away down the stream and out of sight. If your thoughts are racing and you need a higher-paced visualisation, imagine standing on a motorway bridge and dropping each worry onto a speeding car as it drives away beneath you.

Having read, or listened to all this, you might be thinking, "OK Caroline, that's all well and good but what happens when the thing I'm worried about *is* a real thing and *is* happening right now, but it's not exactly a tiger worry because it's not going to kill me?" For example, maybe you're worried about your mum's poor health. Let's say she's developed a persistent cough in recent weeks. This is a right now, real-life worry. What do we do about that?

This is where one of my favourite worry strategies comes in handy: *caring*.

Caring

There's an important difference between worrying and caring. Worrying makes you worried. Caring helps you to care.

Of course, if your mum is ill and you love her, you're going to worry about her. It's the most natural response in the world and we wouldn't want to change that. *Worrying* about your mum, however, is unhelpful in the long run because it makes you feel worse, and it doesn't help you or her.

Thinking over and over about her persistent cough, and what it might mean, might give you the illusion that you're doing something about it, but in fact you're just worrying about it. Worrying takes up an awful lot of time and energy and does nothing to change the situation.

Caring, on the other hand, helps you to think about the ways in which you can help and is a much more peaceful way to hold something in your heart and mind. If there's something worrying you right now, ask yourself: "How could I *care* about this instead?"

In the example I've given – worrying about your mum's health – you might say something like this to yourself: "I care about my mum's health. I think I'll give her a call tonight and check she's been to see the doctor about that cough."

Caring can be a more helpful emotional response to a worrying situation. It means you're still emotionally connected to what's happening, and it can help you to do something useful about it without staying stuck in worry around it. You can care about something, plan to do something about it, and then continue your day focusing on other things.

Perhaps you could *care* about climate change? Or the cost-of-living crisis? Or the many wars happening around the world? Whatever's worrying you lately, try asking yourself: "How can I care about this?" and see what happens.

It's also worth knowing that worry and anxiety can sometimes be a distraction from something bigger in our lives that we're not attending to. Worry can be a distraction from other more difficult emotions such as sadness, fear or anger. If you find yourself worrying more than usual lately, ask yourself these two questions:

"What else is going on in my life that I am not paying attention to?"

"If I wasn't worrying about this right now, what would I be doing instead?"

Give yourself permission to put your worry down for a moment and look beyond it. The answers to these questions, and your responses to the exercises in this chapter, will hopefully help you to worry less, and may just surprise you too.

Note: Sometimes worry can tip into a more serious and persistent state of anxiety. If your worrying is stopping you from sleeping for more than a few nights or interfering with your ability to go about your day-to-day life as normal, then consider speaking to a professional to see if you could benefit from some treatment and support. See the pages on 'Where to get help' at the end of this book or visit our 'Useful Links' page at *www.joyfuldoctor.com*.

6

Permission to grieve

"Grief is the price we pay for love."

Queen Elizabeth II

"I am OK. I am at peace."

Jessi texted me this message, at the age of forty-one, just days before she died.

During the UK's first COVID lockdown in March 2020, my close friend Jessi, a brilliant emergency doctor, environmentalist and poet, received a phone call from her own GP. The biopsy results from the lump in her leg had come back.

"It's melanoma I'm afraid."

We were both doctors and we knew what this meant. We knew of melanoma's aggressive nature and poor prognosis compared to other types of skin cancer.

I was the first person Jessi told. She couldn't face the pain this news would bring to her family. I wanted to jump in my car and race to see her but I couldn't, because the whole country was in lockdown.

Jessi wasn't permitted to see any of her close friends or family in person for weeks after her diagnosis. The best we could give her was support via telephone and video.

As the year went on, the cruelties continued. The never-ending COVID tests to determine if she could attend chemotherapy sessions. The challenge of going for walks in a world where others, who didn't appreciate the risk to her vulnerable immune system, breathed and coughed all over her. The ongoing isolation and the gnawing loneliness of living alone, with no one but her cancer, 'Bob', for company.

Those of us who loved her felt hopeless and restricted in what we could do to help her in her hour of need. When the lockdown guidance relaxed, we spent every possible moment by her side. We watched her processing the awful situation unfolding around her. We sent her packages full of love, raised thousands of pounds to ease the financial strain and tried to be generally useful. But we couldn't stop the inevitable. We watched as this bright, beautiful, vivacious, extraordinary woman drifted closer and closer to death.

As I write this chapter, it's over three years since Jessi died. I'm still grieving her loss profoundly but it's a price I'm willing to pay for having known her in the first place.

Grief is one of the hardest human experiences we go through in life. It's a rollercoaster of different emotions, washing over us in intense waves, sometimes predictably, sometimes not. It takes time, often months or years, to pass. And the feelings of grief can return suddenly, out of the blue, at any moment.

We can feel shocked, in disbelief and denial. We can bargain desperately with God, Allah, or ourselves to bring our loved ones back for just a moment. We can feel depths of sadness we never thought possible and anger so overwhelming we think we might burst. Grief is an exhausting concoction of feelings that can consume whole chunks of our life and leave us changed forever.

I've helped those grieving the loss of a child, parent, partner or pet, and those who've lost a relationship, job, their purpose or a life-long dream. Each grief has taken its own path and left its own unique mark. As with all our human emotions and experiences, grief does not stand still for long. It constantly flows and you cannot rush it; it will take as long as it needs to pass.

Eventually, there will come moments of acceptance, peace and even joy. Moments when remembering those we've lost, and the experiences we've shared with them, can bring us great happiness and solace as we move forward in life.

A metaphor I find particularly helpful when it comes to understanding grief is 'the ball in the box'. Imagine your life is like an empty box. Inside, at the bottom of the box, there is a small button called the 'pain button'. When you lose someone close to you and you start to grieve, it's as if there's suddenly a big heavy ball of grief filling up the whole box. This grief ball is sitting on the pain button, causing you lots of strong, unpleasant emotions and making it very hard to focus on anything else.

What you don't notice at first though, is the grief ball is vibrating and shrinking very slowly over time. At first it feels as if all you can think about is your grief – the ball. But slowly, over time, as the ball continues to shrink and vibrate, it begins to bounce off the pain button for brief moments.

In these moments you experience relief from your feelings of grief for the first time, and this can feel quite strange. It's common to feel guilty in these moments, as if somehow feeling happy again is betraying the memory of your loved one. This is not the case though. There's nothing wrong with feeling good again; it's simply the natural ebb and flow of human grief.

As the grief ball continues to get smaller over time, it starts to bounce around the box more and more, and spends less and less time hitting the pain button. Eventually, over many months or years, the ball becomes so small, and hits the pain button so infrequently, that you may only feel your grief on rare occasions.

However, when something comes along that reminds you of the person you've lost – for example, their favourite song plays on the radio – then BANG! The ball crashes into that pain button again and you're right back where you started. It may only last a few moments but it can feel as painful and intense as it did when the person first died.

At other times, such as the anniversary of their death or a special occasion like their birthday, Ramadan or Christmas, the grief ball may temporarily grow bigger again. It may fill your thoughts more often, only to subside back to its smaller size again as the anniversary passes by.

If you experience another loss, you may find another grief ball bouncing around in your box. Sometimes, multiple grief balls can be bouncing around at the same time, banging into each other and hitting that pain button more frequently.

Although grief balls tend to reduce in size over time, they rarely disappear completely. The trick is to notice, recognise and understand them, and to be kind to yourself when one of your grief balls hits that pain button again.

It can also be helpful to imagine other people's grief balls bouncing around inside their lives. It can help you to feel more patient and compassionate, especially around the anniversaries of other people's losses when they may be more preoccupied and emotional than usual.

If you, or a loved one, find yourselves grieving, give yourselves permission to feel *all* your feelings and to express them in healthy ways. If you're feeling sad, feel sad, cry, mope and talk about the person or thing you miss. If you're feeling angry, feel angry, and let it out in healthy ways that won't hurt you or others. You'll find more ideas on how to do this in chapter 12 'Permission to feel angry'. If you're feeling happy, feel happy; it's OK.

Whatever you're feeling, it's OK. Remember, if you give yourself permission to feel your feelings, your grief will continue to shrink and gradually cause you less pain, over time.

7

Permission to fear

"A life lived in fear is a life half-lived."

Fran
in *Strictly Ballroom* by Baz Luhrmann

It was the week before my month-long medical school elective was due to start in rural Vermont, USA. I was staying with a friend and her family in a beautiful old three-storey brownstone house in the centre of Boston.

"Don't walk across Boston Common after dark. It's dangerous."

I heard the warning from my well-intentioned friend and thought: "That sounds sensible, I'll walk around the edge." However, a few hours later, emboldened by alcohol and in the company of a trusted male friend from medical school, I thought otherwise. I thought it would be OK to walk across the common at night.

The path was clear. A bright moon and low-level artificial lighting lit the way ahead. There was a police car stationed by the entrance to the park, acting as a deterrent to any potential baddies who might be lurking. Even as the man started walking towards us from the other direction, I felt OK.

"It's quite light and I'm with my friend," I thought. "We're less than thirty feet from a police car. He's probably just crossing the common like we are."

As he came closer I started to feel uneasy. I talked more loudly to my friend. Maybe I wanted the man approaching us to hear the subtext of my internal monologue: "I'm not alone. I'm not vulnerable."

As he passed alongside me, I felt my body emit a little sigh of relief. It was OK. He was going to walk right past.

Suddenly my head jerked back.

He'd grabbed my hair and was pulling me backwards.

My friend was oblivious, still talking and walking away, further away. By the time he'd realised I was no longer by his side he was a few feet ahead. He spun around and saw me, head straining to one side, the blade of a pocketknife glinting, held tight against my neck.

It was another of those moments where the world and time stood still. My mind went blank with fear. I couldn't remember any of the self-defence moves my older brothers had taught me to 'toughen me up' over the years. I just froze. All I could feel was the blade of the knife pressing against my neck. I remember thinking: "This could be it. There's nothing I can do."

"Gimme your money!" the mugger shouted.

"OK, take it easy, here you go…" my friend shouted

back, slowly reaching into his pocket to get his wallet. He gathered all the notes he had and then, without warning, threw them on the ground at our feet. He told me later that he'd hoped the mugger would release me to pick the money up off the floor. But he didn't, he just got angry.

"What are you f**king doing? Pick it up!" he shouted at my friend.

He was insulted and angry – not what I wanted my mugger to be. He had all the power here and he didn't like being disrespected. I could sense it and I was *very* scared.

"*Please, please*, just pick up the money and give it to him," I pleaded with my friend. Thankfully, he complied. He quicky gathered up the money and passed it to the mugger. As he did so, the mugger's grip on my hair eased just a fraction, enough to give me a glimmer of hope.

"I might survive," I thought.

He demanded my money too and I frantically scrabbled in my bag and gave him everything I had. He took the money, looked about him, and then jogged off quite casually in the direction of the police car.

"Are you OK?" My friend was in front of me now. "Quick! The police car!" he shouted.

Dazed and confused, we rushed to the spot where the police car had been. It was still there.

"We saw him jog by," they said. "Quick, get in, we'll find him." Hope and relief started to grow. We were going to be safe and we might even catch the person who did this.

"Didn't you know the common was dangerous?"

My mind was too scrambled to notice the victim blaming in that question. It triggered a wave of shame in me as we sat quietly in the back of the police car and they continued to fire questions at us.

"What did he look like?" "Where are you from?" "Where are you staying?"

They asked a lot of questions and we answered them all as best as we could.

My eyes were darting from side to side, searching outside the car for the man who'd just mugged me, and inside the car for the hidden camera that had to be there in this increasingly bizarre movie-like scene.

As we drove around, our hope of catching the perpetrator dwindled with every passing moment. The surreal gradually gave way to the real and I started to long for the comfort and safety of a familiar place.

Eventually, we all agreed it was unlikely we'd find the mugger that night and the police drove me back to the home of the friend I was staying with.

She looked so concerned when she saw me standing on the doorstep, shaking and crying, a police car flashing its lights in the background. She and her husband were incredibly kind and only once said: "Didn't we tell you the common was dangerous?"

I'll never forget how they helped me that night.

My friend's husband handed me a glass of whisky, and my friend, a recovering alcoholic, concerned that my drinking may have played a part in the night's events, offered to take me to a meeting of Alcoholics Anonymous

(AA) the next day.

She invited me again the next morning.

"Sure, I'd love to go with you," I said. "I'm a medical student. I'd be interested to learn about alcoholism and AA for when I'm a doctor."

Of course, there was absolutely no way I was an alcoholic myself. After all, I didn't drink in the mornings, or drink and drive, and I rarely drank spirits. Never mind that I drank more than was good for me on a regular basis. Never mind that I often woke up the next day regretting what I'd said and done the night before. Never mind that I often drove the morning after a big night out, when my blood alcohol levels were probably still dangerously high.

Nope, I was still firmly in denial at this stage. I believed I was fully in control.

I was very happy to attend an AA meeting though, as an observer. I was fascinated to learn about addictions and how they affected the people who had them. I'd loved my psychiatry placement at medical school the year before, and I thought I might end up doing it as a job one day. The more useful experiences I could grasp like this the better.

The building where the AA meeting was being held looked just like the one in the TV show *Cheers*, which is quite ironic when you think about it – an AA meeting being held in what looked like a famous bar. We walked down the steep external steps and into the basement. There was no bar there though, just a large room and lots of people standing around talking. There were two rows of chairs arranged in semicircles facing a small wooden table with two more chairs behind it facing back. Several slogans were stuck to the walls: "Keep it simple" "Just for today" "Keep coming back".

Everyone started to sit down. I looked around. It was mainly heavily-tanned middle-aged white men, me (a twenty-three-year-old pale white English girl) and my friend. When people started talking, I had the strangest feeling. I felt like a fish out of water who'd finally come home to the ocean.

They weren't talking about alcohol; they were talking about life, *my life*. These men I'd assumed I had nothing in common with were thinking and saying things exactly like I was thinking. They were speaking my thoughts out loud. I could identify with almost everything I heard.

They spoke about feeling restless, irritable and discontent. They spoke about needing something, anything, to make themselves feel better. They spoke about needing help to cope with the 'people, places and things' of everyday life. They spoke about 'normal people' being somehow different to them. They shared honestly the things they didn't like about themselves, including their low self-esteem and their selfish ways.

They shared a little about their experiences with alcohol too. They shared stories of times they'd intended to have 'just one drink' and woke up the next day with no recollection of what had happened next. They recalled how they hadn't realised they were alcoholics until the consequences of their drinking got so bad they couldn't hide from it any longer. They spoke of hitting rock bottom and being forced to admit to themselves that they had a problem. They shared awful stories of things they'd said and done whilst under the influence of drink or drugs, and how many failed attempts they'd made to stop.

They also shared how the fellowship of AA had helped them. How rooms like this one had helped them to stop drinking, take responsibility for themselves and find hope again, one day at a time.

They spoke of a sober life being a better, happier life; one filled with love and service, purpose and gratitude. They looked happy, and well, and... normal.

I still didn't realise what all this meant for me.

I remember thinking I should be more careful when I was drunk, like not walking across a well-known muggers' paradise in the middle of the night. But that was it.

I didn't have a problem with alcohol.

Did I?

No.

That possibility was far too scary.

Scarier than being mugged at knifepoint.

If I was an alcoholic I might have to stop drinking, and nothing scared me more than that.

When we're struggling with a difficult truth about ourselves, or the situation we find ourselves in, it's sometimes easier to deny it completely. Only when the pain of that situation becomes unbearable, and we reach a 'tipping point', do we find ourselves ready to accept the truth and take the action we need.

For me, it was another ten years before the fear of what would happen if I continued drinking outweighed my fear of stopping. At that point I finally accepted I had a problem with alcohol, and with the help of other recovering addicts, I was able to put the drink down, once and for all, one day at a time.

It's OK to be scared, to be afraid, to feel fear. Fear is just a messenger that can lead you to a safer, happier place. If you share your fear with trusted others, you can find the help you need to get better.

Note: All being well, the 30th November 2024, will mark my 10th year of sobriety from alcohol, cigarettes and illicit substances.

8

Permission to be a mess

*"Without anxiety and illness I should have been
like a ship without a rudder."*

Edvard Munch

How many health conditions can one doctor have? The
answer is *unlimited*. Comorbidity – the occurrence of
more than one physical or mental health condition at the
same time in the same person – is common. Being a
doctor doesn't stop you from having multiple health
problems. In fact, doctors can often have more health
problems than the patients they're looking after.

At the time of writing, I'm a working doctor and I have
nearly a dozen physical health conditions including
asthma, diabetes and obstructive sleep apnoea. Like
everyone else, I've also had several acute illnesses or
injuries over the years, like COVID or a broken finger.
There have also been times in my life with additional

health burdens. For example, when I was pregnant and had six pregnancy-related complications, including hyperemesis gravidarum and severe pelvic girdle pain which left me wheelchair bound for two months before the birth of my son.

I've managed all the physical health conditions I've experienced so far in my life with a combination of medication, physical aids, physiotherapy, lifestyle factors, and the support of my friends and family.

I'm not sharing these experiences to show off, or to qualify myself as an expert by lived experience. I'm merely trying to normalise and de-stigmatise health problems amongst doctors. I want to demonstrate that it's possible to have multiple health problems and be a good doctor at the same time.

In addition to multiple physical health conditions, I have also had lived experience of five mental health conditions.

I have bipolar affective disorder (BPAD) – a severe mood disorder which means that, while I am well a lot of the time, sometimes I'm not.

Since my late teens I have had over a dozen episodes of low mood (depression), each lasting six weeks to a year or more, and a few episodes of high mood (hypomania, mania and mixed affective states), each lasting from a few days to a few months. My mood is stable between these episodes and has, thankfully, been relatively stable for many years now.

I make sure I stay well by taking medication, having

talking therapy when I need it, and keeping a gentle eye on lifestyle factors such as stress, sleep and movement.

I am also an addict. I am an alcoholic and a cross-addict in recovery, which means that, without the help of others, I will use a variety of substances like alcohol, cigarettes, and behaviours like work and spending money, to manage my life and emotions in an unhealthy and destructive way.

I stay sober, sane and balanced by abstaining from unhealthy substances and behaviours on a daily basis, attending regular peer support meetings, working a daily programme of recovery and doing service to help other recovering addicts.

I have an eating disorder, which has been my constant companion since the age of eight. Over the years, it has shown itself in excessive dieting, bingeing, purging and over-exercising, to differing degrees at different times. It's thankfully relatively quiet these days.

I stay peaceful around food and kind to my body by not restricting what I eat, not making myself sick or over-exercising, and having talking therapy when I need to.

I have attention deficit hyperactivity disorder (ADHD). Like many successful people, including many doctors, I was diagnosed with this lifelong condition late, in adulthood. My ADHD symptoms have been present since early childhood, but I'd learnt to mask and adapt around them.

My symptoms became more obvious when I treated

my other mental health conditions and I could see my baseline difficulties more clearly. Looking back now, I suspect my undiagnosed and untreated ADHD contributed to some of my earlier difficulties with my mood and substance misuse.

I also have other traits of neurodiversity, for example, a few autistic traits. Autistic Spectrum Disorder is another commonly under-diagnosed condition amongst both women and doctors.[7,8]

I am learning to manage my ADHD and autistic traits by compassionately acknowledging my day-to-day challenges, using strategies to accommodate them, taking medication for ADHD and keeping a gentle eye on lifestyle factors such as stress, movement and sleep.

I have had post-traumatic stress disorder (PTSD) twice. I am a survivor of childhood sexual abuse, and as an adult I have been mugged twice and been in two significant car accidents. I'm also a doctor and, like all doctors, I've been exposed to multiple traumatic experiences directly and indirectly throughout my time at medical school and work. Thankfully, my PTSD responded well to two rounds of active trauma treatment in my mid-thirties and early forties.

I stay well by checking every few months for any signs of relapse, using grounding exercises when I'm feeling unsafe, and getting professional help again when I need to. I also make sure I always have a safe place to talk through any new traumatic experiences as they occur.

Every one of my physical and mental health conditions has one thing in common: to get well and stay well *I need the help of other people.* As a fiercely independent woman and doctor, this hasn't been an easy truth to come to terms with. I see the doctors I support grappling with this same truth every day. We would love to be able to do it on our own, but sometimes we just need help.

When I consider my ever-growing list of physical and mental health conditions, I can sometimes feel overwhelmed by the tangled mess of it all. At other times, I see it as an inspiring run of hurdles I've managed to overcome. In these moments, like an Olympic athlete, I'm spurred onwards and upwards, inspired by what I have overcome.

Sadly, my list of mental health conditions is neither unusual nor uncommon for a doctor, or any human being. In fact, as my wonderful colleague Richard Jones, Clinical Director at NHS Practitioner Health puts it: mental health is the land of comorbidity.

As a psychiatrist and therapist, it's common for me to see doctors with three or more diagnosable mental health conditions active in their life at any one time. Some of us just have slightly more than our fair share.

In this book you will read some of my own stories of experiencing and managing mental health conditions, and those of other doctors doing the same. It's worth remembering that, while a single story may highlight a certain aspect of a person's journey, they may also have other difficulties to contend with. Two people with the same condition may also experience different impacts on their life, and require different approaches to help them.

There are certain mental health conditions that tend to cluster together in both individuals and their families. As a psychiatrist and therapist, I stumble across these clusters in my patients all the time. I often draw them out on a piece of paper, or an online whiteboard, writing each diagnosis in a separate petal of a beautiful flower.

By doing this I can reassure the person affected that I see these 'flowers of comorbidity' in people all the time, and there are things we can do to help with each petal, no matter how overwhelming the whole flower may seem right now.

Together we decide which petal, or combination of petals, to focus on first, to have the biggest and quickest impact with the minimum amount of pain and effort. Sometimes, if we're lucky, there's a condition at the centre of the petals, like trauma or neurodiversity, and if we deal with this condition first, all the other petals start to improve too.

The following is a list of mental health conditions that commonly occur together in the same person or their family members:

- Depression and anxiety
- Bipolar affective disorder, addictions and ADHD
- Obsessive compulsive disorder (OCD), eating disorders and ADHD
- Any two or more anxiety disorders such as OCD, social phobia, agoraphobia, or specific phobias

You may be able to look back in your own family history, or the families of those you know, and see clusters of certain health conditions too.

It's also common for mental health conditions to relapse or recur over time. If this happens to you, it doesn't mean it's your fault, it's just the nature of that illness. With recurring conditions – for example, recurrent depression – we can get better at managing them over time. With experience and support they can come to have less of a negative impact on our life.

When I've been unwell in the past, particularly when depressed, I've often thought 'This is going to last forever,' or 'It won't get better this time.' But I have learnt over time that this is just the negative mood-dependent thinking of depression. The reality is, whatever mood I'm in, there's always support out there if I'm willing to engage with it. There are always things I can do to improve my mental health, even if it's just to say out loud to someone else: "I don't know what to do next. Can you help me?"

Whatever you, or anyone you know, are going through right now, please remember that it will be OK. As they say in the rooms of Alcoholics Anonymous and other twelve-step fellowships: "It will be OK in the end. If it isn't OK, it isn't the end."

9

Permission to lose your mind

"You can learn many things from children.
How much patience you have for instance."

Franklin P. Adams

I never wanted to have children. A part of my soul longed for children but the rest of me wanted to run for the hills. I'd always loved other people's children (the type you can give back) but didn't want any of my own.

I'd seen how hard parenting could be. I had seen my seventeen-year-old best friend lose her youth and sanity to nappies and screaming in a tiny one-room bedsit. I'd seen countless friends become desperate, exhausted, worn-out shells of their former selves after their children were born. I'd seen the enormous impact children had on the adults they were born to, no matter how loved and wanted they were.

I'd also witnessed the pain and devastation of infertility, miscarriage and child death in my own family, and in the lives of my patients. Perhaps most significantly of all, I knew I had the potential to become seriously mentally unwell during pregnancy and following childbirth.

In 2009, while sitting in a dingy classroom at the back of an old asylum building on the outskirts of Cambridge, I heard the story of Dr Daksha Emson and her daughter Freya. That day my fellow psychiatry trainees and I were learning about the perils of the perinatal period. This time in a woman's life, from pre-conception until a year after birth, is fraught with emotional turmoil and an increased risk of maternal and paternal mental illness and death.

Daksha Emson was a bright young psychiatrist who, just a few years earlier, had been learning about perinatal mental health herself. She had a history of bipolar affective disorder which she'd kept hidden from many of her family, friends, and colleagues due to stigma and fear of recrimination. Even her husband didn't know the full extent of her disease.

Daksha became acutely unwell after the birth of her first child. One day, when her daughter Freya was just three months old, Daksha stabbed Freya, then herself, and then set them both on fire. Baby Freya died instantly from her injuries and her mother Daksha died some weeks later in intensive care.

The inquiry that followed their tragic deaths found several fatal flaws in the support systems surrounding doctors with mental illness.[9] It highlighted how doctors were often treated in secret, hidden by shame and stigmatised by the systems designed to protect them.

The inquiry led to the creation of NHS Practitioner Health – a free and confidential mental health service for healthcare professionals. By 2024, this world-leading service, which started by treating one doctor in 2008, had treated its 30,000th clinician-patient. At the time of writing, it receives around 550 to 650 self-referrals from doctors, dentists and other clinicians every month.

I'm very proud to work for this service as a psychiatrist and therapist. We treat the doctors we help as more than just people with professional credentials and a sense of vocation. We treat them as human beings in need of support, and we do this in loving memory of Dr Daksha Emson, her daughter Freya and an ever-growing list of health and care workers who are dying by suicide.

As I sat in that dimly-lit asylum building in Cambridge, hearing the heart-breaking story of Daksha and Freya's deaths, a little voice deep down inside me whispered: "*That could be me one day.*"

I had a sense that, if I ever fell pregnant, it might lead to the beginning of one life, my child's, and the catastrophic disintegration of another life, my own.

At this time I didn't know I had bipolar affective disorder, but I knew there was a chance I could develop it one day. I'd already suffered through half a dozen episodes of severe depression with suicidal thoughts. These long spells of low mood, fatigue and worthlessness, of daily struggle and torment, had stolen years of my life.

I spent much of my twenties living in a swamp of

inactivity and poor self-care. Some episodes were formally diagnosed and treated, while others silently sucked the joy from my life and then quietly retreated before I'd even noticed they'd come to stay.

I learnt that day, hearing Daksha's story, that some women with bipolar affective disorder suffer depressive episodes throughout their teenage years and early adulthood, and then go on to have their first episode of high mood when they have a child.

These women 'go high' when the emotional strain, sleep deprivation, and hormonal changes of pregnancy and childbirth overwhelm their physical and psychological defences. I couldn't help but wonder if that would happen to me.

I knew deep down that I was 'the type' to develop bipolar disorder. If I didn't get enough sleep I became very buzzy, with racing ideas and boundless optimism. I would often finish twelve-hour night shifts as a junior doctor feeling more elated than you might expect.

I had high verbal fluency, and frequent bursts of intense creativity and productivity that would suddenly stop, as I spiralled back down into yet another depressive episode. On hearing Daksha's story, I realised that one day, I too could go high, or dangerously low. I realised that I too could die by suicide.

This is why, in the middle of a psychiatry lecture, at the age of twenty-eight, I finally decided that I would never have a child of my own.

Three years later, I found myself lying in a hospital bed,

drowsy and bewildered, unable to move my legs, and staring at a baby in a plastic cot.

As I lay contemplating my beautiful newborn son, I became uncomfortably aware that I didn't recognise him. He seemed special and perfect, and yet I couldn't understand how he was related to me. I didn't know who he was and, quite disconcertingly, I couldn't name him.

My husband and I had picked out a name for our son before he was born. We'd decided to call him Leo and had told our closest friends and family in preparation for the big day. I was looking forward to that moment I'd seen a thousand times on television, when I'd look down at him and say something like: "Hello Leo, I'm your mummy..."

However, when that moment came, I couldn't do it. I could only call him 'Biffy' – the affectionate nickname we'd given him in pregnancy. Two days crawled by, peppered by frustrating attempts to breastfeed and the midwives cajoling me to give him his proper name.

"We can't keep calling him Biffy!" they protested, as his intended name Leo, lay temporarily and perilously balanced on the front of his cot, on a personalised card from a favourite aunt.

Two days earlier, as the surgeons lifted his tiny, mottled body from my womb, I heard him cry. I recognised his cry. It was like no sound I'd ever heard before but at the same time so familiar to me, and to me alone. I cried with joy at hearing that sound, knowing he was safe, knowing that I loved him. Yet here I lay, just two days later, with a total stranger laying in the cot beside me.

The demons encircled my bedroom. I sat bolt upright, gripping the side of my bed, staring wide-eyed and petrified. The hooded figures were taunting me, just out of sight, there one moment and gone the next.

"There!" I screamed at my husband, pointing, panicking.

"There's nothing there, it's OK..." came the soothing yet unnerved reply of my husband, stroking my arm, trying to calm me.

"There!" I shouted again, pointing at the curtains.

Curtains?

Were they just curtains?

No, they can't have been. I saw demons.

They were demons...weren't they?

Slowly, as my fevered mind found its way back to itself and my heart stopped racing, I reassured myself with some basic facts of psychiatry I'd learnt at work. When waking from, or drifting off to sleep, the brain can often see 'illusions' that appear real – for example, a demon in the curtains. These are called hypnopompic and hypnagogic illusions respectively.

With an illusion, you know it's not real, like when you see a shape in the clouds or a figure in your tea leaves. This was different. I was on the edge of madness, and I knew it. I couldn't say for certain that these demons weren't real. If I'm truly honest, as I recall them now, they seem as real to me as they did that day.

My circling demons.

"Where's my dressing gown cord? Have you seen it? It can't have disappeared."

"I haven't seen it," my husband replied.

A few hours earlier I'd confessed to one of the nurses that I was having thoughts of hanging myself in the shower room with that dressing gown cord.

Could that be why I couldn't find it? Had they taken it away from me to keep me safe? Was it sitting in a locked drawer somewhere to put *their* minds at ease?

I never found out what happened to that dressing gown cord. It was part of a beautiful kimono I'd bought in Tokyo, on the way home from two years working as a junior doctor in Australia. Every time I see the new, less beautiful cord I bought to replace it, I remember that day. I think about how close I came to dying by suicide like Dr Daksha Emson did.

I am also reminded of my secret tattoo (yes, mum and dad, I have a tattoo...) It's a small and discrete tattoo of a punctuation mark, a semi-colon, inspired by Project Semicolon.[10] It's a visual reminder that, rather than putting a full stop on the sentence of my life, I chose to put a semi-colon instead; I chose to live.

I'm disappointed I lost my favourite dressing gown cord that day, but I am so grateful I didn't lose my life.

"This can't be right," I thought.

I looked down and counted thirty-two separate breakfast items on the table in front of me. It was the morning after my dressing gown cord had disappeared and another twenty-four hours had gone by without sleep.

I was feeling unusually happy and was so excited by the maternity ward's breakfast buffet that I'd made over twenty separate trips from the buffet table to my plastic dining table and back. I wanted to sample every flavour of yoghurt, every type of cereal, and every combination of fruit juice available. I wanted to drink it all in like a visual feast.

It was all so colourful, so fun and so inviting. I wanted one of everything, and I wanted to play with it all. I was lost in a world of possibility and excitement. I had no appetite but every conceivable combination of food in front of me. I was so happy. Until I wasn't. Until I realised what I'd done. Even for someone with a life-long eating disorder this was unusual behaviour.

"I don't know what I'm doing."

"I'm not fully in control anymore."

"Everything is too much."

"Maybe I'll have to go to the specialist mother-and-baby unit after all."

My thoughts tumbled on, as jumbled and unnerving as the overwhelming breakfast selection on the table in front of me.

Later that day I was holding the doctors and nurses, along with my husband and mother, hostage in my hospital side room.

"I can understand why people run down the street naked... I'd like to run down the ward naked... how funny is that! How crazy is that? What's happening to me? I've read about this... this is what *being high* feels like… this is how my patients with bipolar behave… when they're high, or mixed… I can't be high… I want to die… This is what we need to do… I know I'm speaking quickly but I think we have a window of opportunity here... I need to see the on-call psychiatry team… and we must go 'low-stimulus'… I mustn't be allowed to do too much… or see too much… or be interrupted too much… I must sleep... we must take this seriously…"

On I went grandiosely explaining to my concerned hostages what needed to be done for my mental health. It was no longer clear to me what I was saying out loud and what was just in my head. By the looks on the faces of my audience it wasn't clear to them what was going on either.

"I *know* you see, I'm a psychiatrist. I know how to make a good plan..."

My 'out loud' voice was becoming a little too loud now, a little too insistent, and very difficult to interrupt. My mother looked at me from the corner of the room with a mixture of pity and fear in her beautiful blue eyes. She looked close to tears, unable to recognise the daughter she loved so much.

Everyone was nodding politely and going along with the charade, as if it was normal that I should be running the ward round from my hospital bed. Of course, it was not normal; not normal at all. They knew it, and deep down I knew it too.

The voice inside my head was shouting now, "Stop, Caroline! You know this isn't right. Stop talking!", while the voice coming out of my mouth continued to hold court like the Queen of England.

That year, 2012, the year of the London Olympics, I lost my mind and I gained a son. A bundle of pure joy and innocence, with a smell so intoxicating I still catch my breath when I drink him in. He might become someone I don't recognise again from time to time, but he will always be my son. My beautiful boy, Leo.

I never wanted to have children, but I want the children I have. My son and stepdaughter are so precious to me, I find it hard to imagine my life without them in it. Parenting is just as hard as I always thought it would be, but fortunately, it is also incredible in ways I hadn't foreseen.

Of course, I worry that my children will read this book one day and be left thinking that I never wanted them. If that day does come, I'll try to face their reckoning with courage and vulnerability. I'll tell them my truth. No, I didn't want children, but from the moment I knew them, I wanted them, and I have loved them.

In fact, as my mum still says to me from time to time, in the words of Shakespeare: I love them *"more than words can wield the matter"*.

Note: I hope that my children will grow up, able to be courageous in accepting and sharing *their* own truth, whatever that may be. I hope they can give themselves permission, to be who they are, want what they want, and feel what they feel. I must be me, and you must be you. For without that honesty, there is only pain.

10

Permission to feel shame

"Shame cannot survive being spoken."

Professor Brené Brown

"Doesn't handle stress well."

Those four little words shot at me like a shame grenade from the computer screen.

I was a first-year psychiatry trainee, recently returned from a month of sick leave for depression, and I was feeling quite proud of myself that day. Having faced up to my depressive illness and made a relatively speedy recovery, I was back at work again, ready and able to help others who were sick and wounded.

My colleague feedback for the past few months had just landed in my inbox, and amongst all the heart-warming and encouraging praise came those four little anonymised words: *"Doesn't handle stress well."*

Those four little words triggered me into an intense shame storm faster than I could think. My stomach lurched into my throat. I felt sick. My face burned and I wanted the ground to swallow me whole.

It didn't matter that the other fifteen comments on the form were all glowing and positive. It didn't matter that I could describe many good examples of how I'd handled stress well in that job. I just felt shame. My head filled instantly with damaging assumptions. "Someone thinks I'm a terrible doctor." "I'm not good enough." "I can't do this job anymore." "I can't handle stress, apparently."

"Doesn't handle stress well."

Those four little words kept going around and around in my brain, like a faulty washing machine on a never-ending spin cycle, for days.

Like many doctors, when I receive a piece of negative feedback or criticism, my shame response is easily triggered. Like the time someone wrote on a feedback survey that I had a "fixed smile that made me look unapproachable", or the time someone felt they were "being lectured at by a maiden aunt". These singular, passing comments ought to have been drowned out by the hundreds of positive comments surrounding them, but they weren't.

I instantly take these criticisms to heart, as pieces of evidence that prove I am an unworthy, horrible, awful person, a bad doctor, a bad mother, speaker, role model, you name it. It doesn't matter how many positive comments I receive alongside them. Shame zeros in on the words that hurt the most and won't let go.

These negative comments trigger an intense physical and mental reaction in me that I've learnt to call a 'shame storm'. I feel instantly hot and my face flushes. I feel sick to my stomach and my whole body feels uncomfortable. My mind races into overdrive, rehearsing all the things I could have said or done differently. I start listing all the different ways I'm fundamentally a bad person. To add insult to injury, my mind endlessly repeats whatever critical phrase or event triggered the shame storm in the first place.

Thankfully, I've learnt that I'm not the only person to experience intense shame reactions like these. It can happen to all of us. We might be triggered by different things and experience different physical sensations, but we all feel shame sometimes. And shame always feels horrible.

There are many brilliant people researching, writing and speaking about shame. These brave souls are bringing shame out of the darkness, into the light where it cannot survive. Professor Brené Brown, American researcher and storyteller, is one of those people. In the world of shame and vulnerability research she is, quite simply, a goddess. In her multi-million-viewed TED talks and best-selling books, she teaches us that to overcome shame we must first embrace our vulnerability, and to do this we must have courage.[11]

Shame is an ancient human survival response. It's what we feel in response to social threat, and it can feel catastrophic, no matter how small the trigger. Back when we were living in caves and our survival depended on tribal unity, the prospect of being disowned by our family or community was literally life-threatening. Put simply, if other people didn't like us, we might die. The prospect of being shunned or denied food and shelter, led to a severe emotional reaction: shame.

This feeling of shame was designed to keep us pleasing others to stay alive. Unfortunately, this sensitive protective mechanism has persisted in the human brain to this day, when social threats are often much less dangerous. For example, I'm not likely to die from one person out of two hundred saying I have a fixed smile on a webinar, am I? But my brain and body might still react to reading those words *as if I am going to die*. And when someone writes "Doesn't handle stress well" on my colleague feedback form, I might feel as if I am going to die too.

Thankfully, having learnt more about shame over the past few years, I'm now able to recognise and manage it much more effectively. I no longer suffer days of mental torment after a single negative comment from a colleague. Now, when I'm triggered into a shame storm, rather than keeping it to myself and letting it grow inside me, I give myself permission to shine a light on it.

When my shame response is triggered, I'm kind to myself and I acknowledge how horrible it feels. I reassure myself by putting a hand gently over my heart, taking some slow deep breaths and saying something like this out loud: "Woah, I've been shame-triggered. This is a normal shame response. It will pass; it always does. I am safe and I am OK." Then I share my shame storm with a trusted other as soon as I can.

I've learnt that the sooner I share my shame-trigger with someone I trust, the sooner it eases. My worst shame storms have gone from lasting several days to weeks, to passing in a matter of minutes to hours.

Give yourself permission to feel your shame. Name it and gently reassure yourself that it will pass. Share it with someone you trust and watch it start to melt away. Reassure yourself that you're not a bad person; you've simply had your shame triggered. It will pass and it will be OK.

11

Permission to feel overwhelmed

*"You can do anything, but
you can't do everything."*

Anon

I begin writing this chapter as the world stands on the brink of World War III, or at least as close to it as we have knowingly come in my lifetime.

A few days ago, Russia invaded Ukraine, and the twenty-four-hour news cycle has been filled with little else ever since. Last night, after watching a particularly gruesome piece of news footage just before bed, I dreamt that a sniper was trying to shoot me through a small hole in my bedroom wall. Still asleep but petrified, I hurled myself commando-style across the bedroom floor to avoid the speeding bullet.

I came to, cowering in the corner of my bedroom, shaking and terrified, with blood pouring down my leg from a nasty carpet burn I'd sustained during the evasive manoeuvre. Thankfully, I was able to calm myself down quite quickly by reassuring myself it was all just a dream.

Sadly, what was a dream for me remains a daily reality for millions living in war-torn countries around the world. As my carpet burn starts to heal, leaving the faintest shadow of a scar behind, I think of the millions of families torn apart by war, displaced and grieving. Their wounds will be much deeper than mine, and their scars much slower to heal.

This is a good example of how the struggles of others can help to put our own problems into perspective. This is usually a good thing, but I'm left wondering if this can also be unhelpful sometimes, particularly when it comes to healthcare workers looking after their own health.

In the weeks after Russia invaded Ukraine, I noticed myself, and a lot of other doctors, minimising our own struggles by comparing them to the struggles of those affected directly by the war. Of course, this is a natural thing for compassionate human beings to do.

It's normal to want to help those less fortunate than ourselves, especially when images of their pain and suffering are being beamed into our living rooms and onto our smartphones twenty-four hours a day. Focusing on the suffering of others can also help to take our mind off our own problems.

As doctors, however, we don't just compare our struggles to others when a significant event, like a war, breaks out. Pain and suffering don't just appear on our screens during times of international crises. We experience trauma, pain, grief, uncertainty, panic, fear, abuse and violence in our everyday working lives. The horrific stories of death and upheaval, common in war, are also common occurrences for a GP tending to the health needs of a local community, or a doctor stitching people back together in an Emergency Department.

Trauma and suffering are a part of everyday life for a healthcare professional. Therefore, if we choose to compare and defer our struggles and needs to the struggles and needs of others, we can end up doing this *every day*. We can leave late from work every day. We can work through our lunch break every day. We can lose sleep, miss family occasions, miss meals and not drink enough water every day. All because we're putting the needs of others before our own.

I hear phrases like these from doctors all the time:

"How can I take time off when my patients need me?"

"How can I complain when my patients have it harder than I do?"

"How can I leave on time when my colleagues are all staying late?"

In these and hundreds of other ways doctors routinely bury their own pain, minimise their own challenges and ignore their own needs in deference to the needs of others.

Another common phrase I hear from doctors is:

"I feel guilty for taking up your time when there must be others who need you more."

This is my reply, for them, and for you if you've ever felt this way, whether you're a doctor or not.

You are worthy of love and attention. You deserve to have help and support. *You* are the most important person in your life. You are valuable and you have a right to be cared for, just like anyone else. This is your time. It's OK to think about you. It's OK to have your own needs met.

Many doctors carry a hidden burden of untold stories. Stories of trauma, grief, pain and overwhelm. They juggle stressful jobs, unsustainable workloads, inadequate resources, parenting and caring responsibilities, along with all the usual day-to-day annoyances of modern human life.

Doctors aren't immune to days when everything goes wrong. They aren't spared from broken boilers, flat tyres, spilt milk, lost possessions, cat vomit, burnt fingers, family squabbles and disturbed sleep. They must manage these challenges like anyone else, and then go about their day job: dealing with sixty unwell patients in under four hours, scrubbing in for a complex eight-hour operation or helping develop the next life-saving vaccine.

Doctors in developing countries or emergency zones often face the added pressures of working in squalid and dangerous conditions with inadequate medical supplies or human resources to do their job. I'm not saying that doctors have it harder than anyone else, but they do a difficult job and, sometimes, they too can feel overwhelmed.

I have felt overwhelmed many times in my life. I remember a day, a couple of years ago, when our boiler had broken down during a cold spell and we had friends coming to stay for the weekend. We didn't have heating or hot water and we hadn't had time to shop for any food. I'd had an emotionally heavy day at work with several of my patients grieving profound losses at the same time.

I went upstairs to get changed after work and the temporary clothes rail I was using instead of a wardrobe collapsed, spewing my clothes all over the floor. I sat down on the edge of my bed and burst into tears.

My husband heard me sobbing from another room and came through to comfort me. I was a jabbering wreck, spurting out random words in amongst choking back the sobs.

"Boiler!" Sob. "No food!" Sob. "Rail collapsed!" Sob.

My husband put his arm around me and gently repeated, as he has learnt is helpful to do in these moments, "It's OK. It's going to be OK. Just let it out..."

My head was swimming with all the different things I was stressed about in that moment. I couldn't think straight, and I didn't know where to start to feel better. It felt overwhelming.

Thankfully, through the sobbing and spurting, I started to remember a technique that had helped me many times before in these overwhelming moments. It's called: The Whirlwind.

The Whirlwind

In moments of overwhelm, I visualise myself standing in the centre of a whirlwind. I visualise all the things that are stressing me out, whirling around me at ferocious speed. All the people, problems, jobs, deadlines, all of it.

I visualise myself in the quiet centre of the whirlwind, standing firm with both feet on the ground. I start to feel centred, empowered and calm, as everything else continues to swirl around me. I feel the power of the storm and I notice how easy it would be for me to get sucked back into it again. Sometimes it takes all my effort not to get sucked back into the whirlwind.

I take some long deep breaths. I stand or sit very still. I do nothing. I don't try to fix any of the problems or make any of it go away. I just visualise myself standing there, calmly, as the whirlwind rages on around me.

As the feeling of stillness and calm at the centre of the whirlwind starts to spread through me, I start to remember that the storm *will* pass. It always does.

When the whirlwind starts to slow down or it blows away, I can see things more clearly again. I can breathe more gently. The things that were overwhelming me just a few moments ago become things that can be sorted out, or things that don't really matter in the fullness of time. I can start to make a sensible plan for what to do next.

In the example above, I was able to fix my broken clothes rail and hang my clothes back up where they belonged. I then texted my friends to ask them to bring warm clothes for the weekend and look forward to a takeaway or two. I made a note to talk to my supervisor about my grieving patients, then made myself an easy dinner and went to bed.

Like many people, I tend to get overwhelmed more easily when I'm tired, and an early night or two can really help to perk my resilience levels up. I often insist that it won't help, but it usually does.

Sometimes, when I use the whirlwind visualisation, I find myself overwhelmed in a different way. As I stand calmly in the centre of the whirlwind, I can be overpowered by a different emotion such as sadness or anger. I might burst into tears or want to lash out at something. It's as if, in that moment, any sadness, injustice or pain that I've been avoiding by keeping busy, finally has permission to surface.

Occasionally, I find myself filled with a more pleasant emotion in the centre of the whirlwind: a deep sense of gratitude. That's what I felt as the conflict in Ukraine escalated. I had a swirl of difficult emotions triggered by watching the awful scenes of war unfolding on TV and I used the whirlwind technique to manage these. As images of death and displacement streamed into my life and all around me, I stood grounded and calm in the centre of the storm, feeling immensely grateful for the security and safety of my own family and countryfolk.

I felt grateful that I had a car that could break down and a boiler that could stop working at a moment's notice. I felt grateful that, when my son was in hospital with asthma, I didn't need to worry that the hospital may be blown up at any moment by an enemy missile. l felt grateful that I lived in a country which allowed me to express political views without fear of being imprisoned. I felt grateful for the ability to have dinner with an old friend and make a cup of tea whenever I wanted to. I felt grateful that, in a time of war, I had joyful things to celebrate in my life.

Hearing the Ukrainian politicians and soldiers being interviewed on TV, speaking of freedom and family, I realised they were fighting for the very things I felt grateful for: safety, peace, love.

During our worst moments of overwhelm, it's still possible to connect with feelings of calm, gratitude and joy. Overwhelm, after all, is often just a matter of perspective that can be shifted by a change in focus or physiology or overridden by another more pressing distraction.

One doctor I know uses her own version of the whirlwind metaphor to shift her perspective during moments of overwhelm. She visualises each different issue she's facing as a separate mini whirlwind. She has learnt to notice when she's being sucked into a whirlwind and then gives herself permission to step out of it. She then visualises herself sitting back calmly in an armchair, watching as the various whirlwinds of her life tumble around in the distance, eventually blowing themselves out.

Using this metaphor, she was able to find the peace of mind and strength she needed to manage a coroner's case at work, a sick child, a marital breakdown and the death of a close family member, all within the same week. She still gets caught up in the whirlwinds of her life from time to time, as we all do, but now she has the option to take a step back. She can retreat to the comfort and safety of her armchair anytime she wants to and calmly consider her next move.

We cannot control most of what life throws at us. We cannot control what other people think, say or do. We can't even control our own immediate reaction to events. However, as soon as we become aware of what we're thinking, feeling, and doing, we have a choice. We can choose what we do next.

We can choose how we respond to our thoughts and feelings. We can continue to think the same thing or choose to shift our train of thought. We can continue to breathe shallow, rapid, anxiety-inducing breaths or we can choose to take longer, deeper, more calming breaths. We can continue to think critical, unhelpful, nasty thoughts or we can choose to think more neutral, kind or helpful thoughts.

When I woke from my nightmare that night, terrified and bleeding, having hurled myself across my bedroom floor to avoid being shot, I chose to reassure myself that I would be OK. When my doctor-patient found herself overwhelmed at work one day, she chose to ask the nursing staff to hold back any non-urgent tasks until the following week.

When you next find yourself denying your needs in deference to the needs of others, whether you're a doctor or not, you can choose to put your own needs first. We always have a choice.

Am I saying that all our stress and overwhelm is just 'in our heads'? That no matter what the circumstances are, we can do something about it and should *always* feel happy? Of course not. There are some situations where our choices are genuinely limited, or our flexibility of thinking is restricted by external factors. Drugs and alcohol, for example, may temporarily limit our ability to change our thinking or behaviour. Likewise, mental or physical illness may cause rigid thinking patterns and emotional states that are resistant to change without professional help. Day-to-day factors like hunger, fatigue, anger and loneliness may also make it hard for us to make the choices we'd like to in any given moment.

However, in all these situations, there are still things we can choose to do; things that are in our control. For example, if we choose to experiment with drugs, we can make sure we are with a trusted friend when we do. When we notice we are struggling, we can choose to tell someone and ask for help. We can acknowledge our hunger, fatigue, anger or loneliness and try to meet these needs with compassion.

We don't always have to change how we feel. Sometimes it's helpful to feel our sadness, let our anger out, or sit with our loneliness for a while before trying to relieve it. I only advocate trying to change how you think or feel, if the way you are thinking or feeling isn't serving you well and you want to change it. We always have a choice. Our thoughts and feelings are not necessarily facts. We have a choice in how we respond to them.

We can't always avoid feeling overwhelmed, but we

can choose how to respond when it happens. If we can respond kindly to ourselves in our moments of overwhelm, they can pass more quickly and cause us less pain.

When you're feeling overwhelmed by life, try stepping into the calm at the centre of the whirlwind, or stepping away from it entirely. You are not the storm, and the storm will pass. And if you find yourself in a vicious cycle of being unkind to yourself about how you're handling the overwhelm, and then criticising yourself further for not being kind to yourself, then... welcome to the club, we've had T-shirts made! Keep practising the whirlwind technique and it will get better.

Practise treating yourself with kindness. Focus on progress not perfection. And if you find yourself taking two steps forward and one step back, congratulate yourself for moving forwards overall.

12

Permission to feel angry

*"Holding onto anger is like grasping a hot coal
with the intent of throwing it at someone else;
you are the one that gets burned."*

Buddha

As I walked back from the kitchen, a cup of tea in hand, I noticed a brown envelope sitting on the doormat. It was face down, but I immediately sensed that it was from the Driver and Vehicle Licensing Agency (DVLA).

Given that I'm someone with several mental and physical health conditions, many of which could affect my driving, I've had regular communications with the DVLA over the years, and this year was no different. My three-yearly driving licence review was underway, so I hoped this might be my new licence arriving in the post. I hesitated, wondering whether to open it now or later. Something told me to open it now.

"Dear Dr Walker," OK so far.

"We wrote to you in July of last year asking you to arrange and attend an appointment with your GP and, as you have not done this, we are writing to inform you that your application to drive has been denied and you must not drive."

My heart skipped a beat. My stomach leapt into my throat and my thoughts went into overdrive. I didn't understand. I'd seen every doctor I was supposed to see when I was supposed to see them. At no point had anyone told me I wasn't fit to drive. Someone had clearly made a mistake. One that meant I had lost my right to drive in an instant.

I continued reading. "If you wish to appeal this decision you can lodge an appeal with your local magistrate's court within six months."

"Are you kidding me?" I blurted out, to the empty hallway.

My thoughts started racing at warp speed. They bounced from the important work I had to do that morning, to the places I needed to drive to later that week, to how I was going to deal with not being able to drive for up to six months.

Standing there in the hallway, staring at the letter in my hand like it was a freshly exploded bomb, I felt trapped and unable to move. An important part of my freedom had been ripped away. Somewhere, somehow, something had gone wrong. And now, from the moment I'd read those words, it was illegal for me to drive.

I didn't want to waste a second. I had to correct whatever mistake had occurred to bring this about. I wanted desperately, and instantly, to get my licence back so I sprang into action. I called my GP surgery to confirm I'd spoken with my GP the previous summer and that it was documented in my notes that I had done so. Next, I called the DVLA to explain the situation, hoping they'd immediately correct the error and proclaim me able to drive again.

Two minutes later, after selecting what felt like twenty options in a row on their automated phone system, I was eventually greeted by a robotic voice saying: "We are sorry, but we are unable to take calls at this time."

I then dutifully followed the DVLA's online complaints procedure and made swift and full use of the expandable box on the form to lay out my case. After pressing send I received an automated response saying they would respond to my complaint within ten working days.

"Ten working days! I can't not drive for ten working days!"

I sat back in my chair and noticed that my initial state of shock, fear and overwhelm on opening the letter was rapidly being replaced by an intense feeling of anger swelling up inside me. It was coming fast and I was going to explode.

Luckily, I knew what to do.

I reassured myself that it's normal to get angry. Anyone would be angry in this situation. Then I went to the corner of my office where I have a small and sturdy tub chair with a soft, but firm, cushion sitting prettily on it. I picked up the cushion, took a few slow, deep breaths and whispered the words "planned and safe" to myself three times.

"Planned and safe. Planned and safe. Planned and safe."

Then I started bashing the hell out of that chair like a woman possessed.

I whacked that chair with that cushion like my life depended on it. Repeatedly, viciously, manically hitting it with all my might. I was muttering and shouting, expletives and all, channelling all my anger into that chair, each earth-shattering thump more satisfying than the last.

The chair was safe. I was safe. No one was getting hurt. Nothing would break. I was getting my anger out and it was planned and safe.

In that moment, that beautiful, accommodating, inanimate object, whose day job it was to cocoon my patients and me during moments of profound reflection, was transformed into its heroic alter ego: Anger Chair! Anger Chair stood firm, resolved, and ready to take on its feted duty – to help discharge my pain and anger with minimum risk to myself or others.

I vented and thrashed until I started to think it would never end. What if I got stuck with this cushion and this chair, bashing out my anger for the rest of my life? What if I overpowered Anger Chair? What if I unleashed a rage so powerful that the whole world would become consumed like a zombie apocalypse?

Then a quieter voice from deep inside whispered: "Keep going, Caroline. You know this works, and this will pass. Really go for it. It will be OK. It's planned and safe."

Reassured and empowered, I continued to go for it.

Just when I thought I couldn't take another moment, it started to ease. I felt the muscles in my body relaxing, one after the other, like dominoes. My jaw relaxed, my arms dropped and my breathing, which had become erratic and laboured, started to calm. I was done. There was no more anger in me to get out.

Slightly breathless and a little wobbly on my feet, I slowly walked back to my desk and sat down. I looked down and saw that the cushion was still in my hand. I slowly released my grip and gently plumped it back into shape. The cushion looked back at me as if nothing had happened and a feeling of pride washed over me. I'd managed an intense and uncomfortable moment of anger in a safe, planned and deeply satisfying way.

I centred my body, placing both feet flat on the floor, and took a few slow, deep breaths. I allowed my body the time it needed – just a minute or two – to return to a more neutral physiological state.

My exercise in managing anger was complete. I could now think about how else I would like to respond to the letter from the DVLA, in a calmer and more helpful way.

One of the most common emotions I see in doctors is anger. Their problem often isn't the anger itself, but how they manage their anger and how they feel about being angry. They've often had years of conditioning to think of anger as a bad or unhealthy emotion, one to be avoided or suppressed at all costs. Our culture, religion, family, education, and workplace can all reinforce the message that we must never get angry. Anger is labelled as unprofessional, unseemly or dangerous. If you *do* get angry, whatever you do, you mustn't show it or let it out. Bury it. Deny it. Disguise it.

This conditioned thinking can be so unhelpful. Anger is a completely natural human emotion, just like joy, surprise or sadness. It can be incredibly helpful, even life-saving, in the right circumstances. Anger can alert us to danger and injustice, and often motivates us to act when we need to the most.

I work with my patients and clients to accept anger as a normal and important part of human life. Problems can arise when we try to ignore or suppress it. If we keep pent-up anger inside us, it can turn into uncontrollable rage, anxiety or even depression. We can end up expressing it in unplanned and unsafe ways, and harm ourselves or others in the process.

My example of bashing a cushion against a chair is the opposite of this. I accepted my anger and let myself feel it and express it in a planned and safe way. This allowed me to release my anger when I needed to and channel my remaining energies into more helpful actions.

Learning a bit about anger, and starting a regular and 'as needed' anger practice, could be one of the most helpful things you give yourself permission to do.

Providing you do not hurt yourself or others, there is no right or wrong way to express your anger. Simply make it planned and safe. I want to repeat that so it really hits home. Make it planned and safe.

You may need to try out a few different strategies to start with. It's a bit like trying out different machines at the gym to find out which ones you enjoy the most, and which ones give you the results you want with the least amount of time and effort. Treat it as an 'anger experiment' for the first few weeks, trying out different techniques. Then keep what works best for you as your regular go-to 'anger exercises'.

Think about the ways you've dealt with anger in the past and use these as clues to work out what might work for you as an anger exercise. For example, if you find yourself shouting at people who don't deserve it, you could try shouting into a pillow or in a parked car instead.

If you find yourself punching walls when you get angry, maybe you could punch a punch bag, or the mattress on your bed. If you're someone who throws things when you get angry, you could try throwing something small and soft like a fabric juggling ball or a small teddy bear, against a wall.

You may have some healthy ways you express your anger already, like doing angry cleaning or going for an angry walk / run. We all express our anger in different ways and that's OK. Remember: just keep it planned and safe.

Personally, I find it helpful to think about expressing anger in three different ways: physically, verbally and by writing or drawing.

I express my anger physically by punching, pushing, shoving or throwing things. I have learnt, for example, that when I get suddenly angry, if I spend a few minutes punching a soft but firm surface, like a sofa cushion, this works quickly to release my anger. It gets my anger out without hurting me or anyone else.

If I can't do this immediately, because it isn't appropriate or safe, I simply acknowledge I'm angry and give myself permission to take it out on a sofa cushion later that day. Even just acknowledging I'll do this can help release some of the tension I feel in that moment.

I express my anger verbally by screaming and shouting. Again, I choose to do this in a safe place and at a safe time, on my own. I either shout into a pillow or cushion, or I shout in a parked-up car away from others. If I'm somewhere I may worry others with my shouting, I use a technique I call 'silent shouting'. I make all the motions of shouting or screaming without letting out any noise. This may sound and look a little strange but believe me, it works.

Why not give it a try? Find somewhere safe to do so, then simply take a deep breath, prepare to silently shout or scream and go for it. You might like to gesticulate wildly with your arms at the same time. I find this really helps speed things along. Again, remember to keep it planned and safe.

When it comes to expressing my anger in written form, I use a technique called 'no-send writing'. When I get an uncontrollable urge to write an angry email or message to someone, I write it out but I don't send it. I call this writing a 'no-send email' or a 'no-send message'.

I include exactly what I want to say without phrasing it in nice language or holding back. I know that I'm the only one that will ever read it. It gets the emotion out of me, through the pen or keyboard, onto the page or screen, allowing it to dissipate without harming anyone or making the situation worse. This leaves my head clearer and more able to focus. I can then think about how I'd like to respond to what's triggered me in a calmer and more constructive way.

How might you express your anger in these three ways: physically, verbally and by writing or drawing?

Physically

Are you a puncher, kicker, hitter or thrower? How could you do this in a way that won't hurt you or others? Could you get a punch bag? Or play a game of squash? Or stamp on some empty cardboard boxes?

Verbally

Do you like to scream, shout, pant or exhale forcefully?

Not sure? Then give each of these a try. Experiment in a safe space, at a planned moment, where you won't worry any passers-by, and really go for it!

Writing/Drawing

Do you find yourself writing and sending angry emails and text messages that you later regret? Why not try writing a 'no-send' email or message instead? Write it in a notebook or notes section on your phone or computer – somewhere where you won't accidentally send it to someone by mistake.

If writing doesn't appeal to you, you could try angry drawing or scribbling on a piece of paper instead. Remember the key is to get the anger out of you, not to send it out or give it to others. You can shred your writings, delete them, bin them, recycle them, burn them or even post them in a blank envelope addressed to nobody – whatever feels good for you.

If none of these ideas strike you as tempting or possible, then get creative. It just needs to work for you. I once worked with a doctor who liked to break up pieces of old furniture with a baseball bat in her garden (wearing safety goggles of course). Another I know throws juggling balls at a blank bit of wall in her flat. Another one likes to angrily spring-clean their entire house. Several doctors have sent me their 'no-send' angry messages over the years, which I always enjoy reading!

If you'd like to build your own anger practice, start

gently and experiment to find out what works best for you. Build in regular exercises to keep on top of things and 'as needed' exercises you can use in an emergency.

Living with unmanaged anger is like living with a large pressure cooker inside you. As the pressure and steam builds up, the lid keeps popping off. This can happen at random times, spurting hot water everywhere. When you start to let out some of the steam, deliberately and safely using planned anger exercises, the pressure in the cooker reduces and the lid no longer pops off uncontrollably.

Instead, the hot water (your anger) gently bubbles away inside, and you can choose when to take the lid off and let some anger out. You will start to feel more in control of your anger and can learn to use it in more appropriate and healthy ways.

If you suspect you've built up a lot of anger over a long period of time, remember it can take a while to tap off the pressure in your pressure cooker. The pressure may have built up so gradually that you don't even realise how much there is until you start to release it. You might need to do three or four planned anger sessions a week for a couple of weeks to reduce some of that pent-up rage before it starts to settle. Extreme anger can take even longer than this.

Once you start to feel your general levels of anger dropping, you can drop your anger practice down to once or twice a week, and eventually to just as and when you need it.

When I first started using anger exercises, I did them

for half an hour a day for a couple of weeks. Now I only need to do them once or twice a year when I'm caught off-guard by something (like a letter from the DVLA). Sometimes I'll use one when my frustration levels have been gradually building up for a while, or when I notice I'm a bit more irritable than usual. When this happens, I use a favourite 'as needed' anger exercise quickly and effectively to bring me back to my normal self in just a few minutes.

Why not give it a try? You may even enjoy it. Remember to make it planned and safe so it doesn't hurt you or anyone else. And please let me know if you come up with any helpful new ways to express your anger - I'm always looking for good examples to share with others.

Note: In case you're curious, I got my driving licence back after two and half weeks. It turned out to be a mistake on the part of my doctors' surgery. The DVLA processes were generally fair and their staff were very kind and competent. They resolved my complaint as quickly as they could. They hold more than fifty million driver records, and I'd be a bit of a hypocrite if I didn't give them, and my doctors' surgery, permission to be imperfect sometimes.

13

Permission to feel guilty

"Guilt is good. It proves you're not a psychopath."

Dr Caroline Walker

When the COVID pandemic came along, those of us looking after the wellbeing of healthcare professionals were prepared for it to have an extraordinary impact. We knew that doctors, nurses and allied healthcare professionals the world over would struggle with significant levels of stress, anxiety, trauma, burnout and grief.

We knew how human beings typically react in stressful situations like pandemics and could prepare ourselves to support them with their various emotional needs. What we didn't see coming was the avalanche of *guilt*.

Guilt is a normal human emotion that can take different forms. Often, we feel guilty when we do something wrong, like tell a lie or make a mistake that hurts someone. We can also feel guilt when we're ill; for example, when we're depressed and preoccupied by self-critical thoughts, we might think we're a terrible person and that we are doing 'everything wrong'. The avalanche of guilt in healthcare professionals that appeared during the first wave of COVID, was most like the latter. It was guilt related to a sense of doing something wrong, but most of the time the person hadn't done anything wrong, they just *thought* they had.

Some doctors felt guilty for staying at home to safeguard their own or their family's health. Others felt guilty for being at work and putting their families at risk by potentially bringing the virus home to them. Some felt guilty for not taking on extra shifts when they were already exhausted, or for leaving work on time to attend to other responsibilities when there was still work to be done.

Some doctors felt guilty for not delivering the highest standard of care possible because the resources were simply too stretched or not there to begin with. Others felt generally guilty for not being all things, to all people, at all times. There was guilt for being on maternity leave, for taking a career break, or for having recently retired at a time when their country's healthcare system needed them the most.

There was even guilt for enjoying aspects of the pandemic on a professional level – for feeling re-energised and impassioned by the call to action and the increased sense of autonomy that came with it. There was guilt for the feeling of pride that came from being in the right place at the right time and having the specialist skills to help people the most.

You name it, healthcare professionals were feeling guilty about it, and they were talking about it more openly than ever before. These professionals were not actually doing anything wrong. They were just compassionate human beings with difficult choices to make, and they were left feeling guilty about it.

Guilt amongst healthcare professionals is not a new phenomenon. We commonly see it when a clinician needs to take sick leave for a mental health problem. They often feel like they're letting their colleagues and patients down, that they're doing something bad or wrong by taking time off, or that they're somehow a 'bad person' for not being able to do their job.

This 'sick leave guilt' as I call it, will often settle with some simple reassurance, permission and time. It nearly always settles once the clinician starts to get better, and they start to realise just how much they needed the time off in the first place. They can even end up feeling proud of having taken time off, realising that good self-care makes them a better clinician in the long run. However, I also know that there are many doctors out there still feeling guilty for taking time off, and I hope that for some at least, this chapter, and indeed this whole book, may help to ease that guilt.

The wave of guilt I noticed when COVID hit felt different to the usual guilt I saw in doctors. It wasn't just an individual doctor feeling guilt for their predicament, it felt like the entire healthcare profession was in the grip of a more pervasive sense of guilt. Even those of us helping in every way we could felt that we weren't doing enough. Everywhere I looked, another doctor was beating themselves up for the impossible decisions they had to make.

I remember one doctor telling me about a patient on their ward who had tested positive for COVID and was very unwell. The patient deteriorated suddenly and went into cardiac arrest. The doctor was on the ward when it happened, and they instinctively rushed towards the patient to help. Suddenly alarm bells sounded in their head and they stopped in their tracks. They realised they weren't wearing the necessary personal protective equipment (PPE) to keep themselves and others safe.

The ward had run out of PPE earlier that morning. The doctor stood frozen, in a moment that felt like an eternity, confused and tormented, unsure what to do. Every fibre of their being wanted to save the patient's life. They wanted to start CPR and advanced life support, but they knew they'd risk getting COVID themselves if they did.

There was no vaccine at this time. Doctors and nurses around the world were dying from COVID in alarming numbers. Even if they survived it, they could pass it on to so many other patients, healthcare professionals, and their loved ones, potentially causing many more deaths. At the very least they'd need to immediately isolate and be off work for a minimum of ten days, preventing them from saving dozens of other lives in that time.

In that moment, profoundly difficult questions raced through the doctor's mind: "Do I help the patient who's dying in front of me despite the fact I don't have adequate PPE?" "How can I live with myself if I don't try to help them?" "How can I live with myself if I get COVID and pass it on to my other patients, my colleagues or my family?" "How can I sacrifice the one life in front of me for the many more I could save?"

The pain and moral injury that doctor suffered in that excruciating moment summed up what an entire generation of healthcare professionals experienced around the world.

Guilt was everywhere in those early weeks of the pandemic. Every conversation was either directly related to guilt, or guilt was lurking somewhere in the background. I sensed that simple reassurance wasn't going to be enough to fix it this time. We needed permission to try a different approach to managing our guilt when stuck in such impossible situations.

I gave myself permission to stop and think about guilt for a while. And the more I thought about it – what guilt means to us as human beings and why it's so common amongst healthcare professionals – the more I realised the standard responses like 'ditch the guilt' or 'you shouldn't feel guilty' weren't going to cut it. We needed a radically different approach. We needed to *embrace* our guilt, to fully accept it and to make it a more positive force in our lives.

Guilt is a normal, common and even helpful emotion to have. Feeling guilty means that you care. To put it another way, if you feel guilt, it means you are not a psychopath.

Think about it for a moment. If you didn't care about other human beings or the consequences of your actions, you wouldn't feel guilt. Guilt shows that you are a good person. It signals that you care and you want to do more.

Guilt feels so unpleasant because it keeps us focused on the things that we aren't doing, or the things we've done wrong. When I realised this, a possible solution to the avalanche of guilt drowning healthcare professionals came to me. Instead of trying to dismiss our guilt or get rid of it, maybe we needed to accept it and embrace it instead. I realised that by focusing on the positive aspects of guilt we could use it to our advantage. We could use it to gently refocus our attention on what we *were* doing well.

I started to experiment with this idea myself, and with the doctors I was helping, and was pleasantly surprised by the results.

I began by literally patting myself on the back whenever I felt guilty. I reminded myself that I felt guilty because I was a good person and I cared. I started to celebrate my guilt by saying things like: "Feeling guilty means I care about people and I wish I could do more to help them."

Then something surprising and wonderful started to happen. I started to remember all the things I *was* doing to help people, all the things I *could* be proud of. I went from feeling bad about all the things I wasn't doing, to feeling proud of all the things I was. I still cared about the things I couldn't do – I still wanted to help more people and be a better friend, doctor and mum – I just stopped carrying a sense that I was somehow a bad person for not being able to 'do more'. I felt less shame, and I felt less guilt. I felt I was doing enough.

I realised that, in any given moment, I was doing the best I could with the resources I had available to me. I realised that feelings of guilt don't have to leave us feeling hopeless and frustrated. They can help us to feel proud, and refocus us on what we *are* doing to help ourselves and others.

Next time you catch yourself feeling guilty about something – for not doing or being enough, for simply being who you are and making a difficult decision in a challenging world – remember that guilt in this situation is a good thing. Guilt shows you are not a psychopath; it shows you care. Focus on what you *are* doing. Remember that you are doing the best you can with the resources available to you right now.

You are doing enough.

14

Permission to eat

"I am beginning to measure myself in strength, not pounds. And sometimes in smiles."

Laurie Halse Anderson

I slid onto the kitchen floor. I couldn't do it anymore. I couldn't keep eating and hating myself. I couldn't keep making myself sick by sticking my fingers down my throat. I didn't want to cut carbs, count calories or weigh my food anymore. I didn't want to look at food and think of it as good or bad, as allowed or forbidden, as healthy or unhealthy.

From the age of eight I'd looked at food and the way I ate as something to be judged negatively. I worried that there wouldn't be enough for me, and that if I did eat enough to meet my needs I'd become fat and unwanted. I started to label my body as 'not OK'. I looked at pictures of myself and called myself fat and ugly, even though I was neither. I looked at celebrities in magazines and on

TV and thought I needed to look like them to be accepted in the world.

I started to diet, to watch what I ate, and to make choices based on what my culture dictated instead of my own body's needs. I started to talk to myself in critical ways when I was eating, particularly in front of others. I started to eat more in private, hidden away, ashamed and alone.

I stole food from the cupboards at home without asking, always trying to cover my tracks so no one would notice. When I learnt to cook flapjacks as a teenager at school, I would practice making them at home so I could eat even more. I would secretly make twice the amount suggested by the recipe and eat half of the mixture raw while the other half cooked in the oven. I can still taste that sweet, sticky, comforting mixture in my mouth as I remember it now; the way it soothed my feelings, pushing them down, keeping them down, keeping me safe.

When I had plans to eat out I worried about what I would eat. Would I be able to order enough to satisfy me without revealing that I was a 'greedy pig'? Sometimes I would order the 'healthy option' in front of others and then start planning a secret binge at home to make up for it later.

I tried juicing, and souping, and eating nothing but fruit and cereal. I tried eating at certain times of the day, restricting certain foods, measuring portion sizes, and joining slimming clubs to control my weight. I tried taking laxatives and exercising excessively in a bid to rid my body of unnecessary calories and to feel more in control. It was all about control.

One day, in my late twenties, I was driving home from work and I stopped at a mini supermarket to buy some food. In a zoned-out haze I bought a bag of five doughnuts, a large tub of ice cream, a box of cereal and three large bags of crisps. I started eating them before I even got back to my car and continued to eat them on the way home.

At home, I made myself sick to create more room to carry on eating. Eventually I collapsed in a heap on the floor. I felt trapped, doomed to repeat this exhausting cycle, day after day, with no end in sight.

Sometimes I'd catch a break from my disordered eating and feel a brief glimmer of hope. A few days or weeks would go by when my eating was in a relatively peaceful place, but it never stayed that way for long. My eating disorder was always waiting in the wings, ready to take centre stage again.

For over 30 years, barely a day went by without me thinking about food and my body in an unhealthy way. My weight yo-yoed month to month and my moods fluctuated daily depending on how I felt about my food and weight. I oscillated between feelings of exhilaration and pride on a good day, to total self-loathing and despair on a bad day. The numbers on the scale each morning, or how I felt in my clothes, determined my sense of self-worth and how I spent the rest of the day in my head.

On the worst days I would open my eyes and immediately become aware of how 'fat' my body was. As

I rolled out of bed, I berated myself for being so big and unsexy. As I walked across the bedroom floor, I judged my slovenly gait and my chafing thighs. As I sat on the toilet, I started to make resolutions about how good I'd be that day, and how I'd start to turn it all around. Today would be different. Today would be the day I finally pulled myself together. No one would ever know the truth about how lazy and ugly I really was.

By the time I was brushing my teeth, I'd be back to daydreaming about all the foods I could secretly eat to make myself feel better. As I walked down the stairs, I'd be shaming my body with each cumbersome step. As I entered the kitchen to face the daily breakfast gauntlet, I'd often think to myself: "I can't do this anymore."

No one knew this was happening to me. I was keeping it all firmly locked inside. It was my personal shameful experience I couldn't bear to share. To the outside world, it might have looked like I was a fit and slim young woman, eating normally and getting on with the business of life, but on the inside I was tormented. My eating disorder was my constant companion, no matter what size or shape my body was. And it continued, for over twenty years, until I finally plucked up the courage to get the help I needed to recover.

Disordered eating and body image issues are often hidden from others. Someone may appear to be happy and healthy around food and their body image, but they could be carrying a devastating secret torment inside. Disordered eating commonly exists in those with perfectionistic traits, those who feel the need to be in control, or those who feel sensitive to criticism and external pressures. All these traits are common in doctors.

In the world of mental health there exists a sort of unspoken hierarchy of conditions. Some mental health problems come loaded with more shame and stigma than others. Addictions, for example, are high on the list – hence the need for anonymised peer support groups like Alcoholics Anonymous to encourage people to come forward for the help they need. Eating disorders and body image issues are right up there too. They are amongst the most highly stigmatised mental health conditions of our time.

In all the years I was getting help for my depression and other mental health problems, the difficulties I faced around food and my body image were the ones I kept most secret and hidden away. They were also the ones it took me the longest to feel comfortable talking about publicly, and the last I felt able to add to this book.

Although the western medical view on food and body image issues is thankfully starting to evolve, at the time of writing it still causes a lot of problems. For example, the medical world holds fast to a weight-centric model of managing many health conditions, despite there being little evidence for any safe, long-term sustainable weight management options.

There is no health problem known to man that only affects people in bigger bodies. For example, people in smaller bodies can get type II diabetes, sweat rashes and worn-out knee joints, just as those in bigger bodies can suffer from starvation or osteoporosis. However, those in smaller bodies do tend to enjoy the benefit of not being treated with the size-shaming judgements that their bigger-bodied counterparts experience every day.

Doctors of all shapes and sizes can suffer from disordered eating and body image issues. They often also face the self-stigma of feeling that they 'ought to know better' because they are a doctor. They may try to manage the problem alone for many years, as I did, before seeking help.

When they do come forward for help, they can find it extremely difficult to talk about what's been going on for them. They fear being on the receiving end of shame and judgement from the person they tell. I know, I've been there, and I feared it too. Being a therapist didn't stop me from feeling excruciating vulnerability in revealing my truth to my own therapist. Like lots of people, I was scared, and it took a lot of courage to speak up and ask for help.

We also live in a world that promotes disordered eating. Look around you and you'll find the language of weight-shaming is everywhere. It's been woven into the fabric of our societies and healthcare systems: the endless adverts and social media posts portraying the next big trend in 'healthy eating'; the normalised social chit-chat around food and weight in the workplace; the fact that actors and actresses playing leading roles in bigger bodies are asked more often about their body size than the parts they play.

It's taken me years to unlearn the damaging beliefs around food and body image I've accumulated over my lifetime. I am still working on it today. I regularly have to remind myself that I have permission to eat, and to eat for lots of different reasons.

I have permission to eat out of hunger or nutritional need. I have permission to eat in celebration or to comfort myself. I have permission to eat simply for the pleasure of enjoying food. That permission doesn't change from one day to the next based on arbitrary factors like the weather or my waist size. It's a basic human right.

I also remind myself that I have permission to move my body in ways I enjoy. I have permission to meet all my body's needs, even when they may be conflicting. My mouth may want something different to my brain, my bowels or my pancreas, and that's OK. Eating isn't something to fear or be ashamed of, and neither is my body or yours, whatever shape and size they may be today.

If you can identify with anything I've mentioned in this chapter, and you're wondering if you may have a problem with your body image or disordered eating, then please know that you are not alone and there is help out there for you.

You might like to start by gently exploring the avenues of support available to you. Start to consider if there's someone you trust in your life that you could open up to – maybe a friend, a family member or your GP – someone you know who'll respond with kindness. Maybe check out one of the useful webpages in the 'Where to get help' pages at the end of this book. Or maybe you'd prefer the support of an anonymous peer support group like Anorexics and Bulimics Anonymous, or to work with a qualified therapist one to one, face-to-face or online.

Whatever you choose to do, you don't have to rush it. The chances are that your difficulties have been around for many months, if not years, already. It will take a little time to start the healing process and to fully recover. Give yourself permission to go gently and take it one step at a time.

There'll be good days and bad days – days when you can see the end is in sight and days when you feel as if you're right back at square one. That's a normal part of recovery from these challenging issues.

Please remember that you're not alone and that any shame you feel does not belong to you. We're all swimming in the same water. You weren't born hating your body or struggling with complex thoughts, emotions and behaviours around food. Any shame or stigma we feel belongs to the water we're swimming in, not to us as the fish swimming in it.

Give yourself permission to get help – to get the support you need to start untangling what's going on in your head.

Give yourself permission to enjoy moving your body and looking after yourself in healthy ways.

Give yourself permission to eat.

15

Permission to feel disappointed

"We must accept finite disappointment,
but never lose infinite hope."

Martin Luther King, Jr.

Disappointment is not a sexy emotion. It doesn't get talked about, role-modelled or researched nearly as often as the other more popular emotions like happiness, anger or love.

It's the feeling we get when something we hoped for, or expected, doesn't happen, or when something we didn't want to happen does. It often goes hand in hand with failure, self-reproach and the stark realisation that we're not fully in control of our lives. We can find it hard to talk about and hard to manage.

Disappointment is very similar to grief in many ways which, as I shared in chapter 6 on 'Permission to grieve', is one of the hardest experiences a human being can go through. Despite this intensity of feeling, we often tend to ignore or minimise our disappointment, comparing it to the suffering of others which is invalidating and unhelpful.

To add insult to injury, disappointment often leads to other unpleasant, low-energy emotions such as hopelessness and despair. Because it's so unpleasant we often jump, unconsciously, to more proactive emotions and thought processes like anger and worry. This happens so quickly and subtly that we don't even realise the whole thing started with feelings of disappointment in the first place. Unlike typical grief reactions where we're usually starkly aware of the thing we've lost, with disappointment we may not even realise we've lost anything at all.

Let's take the example of failing an exam, which, despite being a doctor, I've done many times in my life. In my experience, when I find out I've failed an exam, I jump straight to feeling angry at myself for not preparing enough or angry at the exam process for being so unfair. Then I immediately start worrying about the impact this will have on my future, and what others will think of me when they find out.

Anger and fear are both perfectly natural reactions in this situation and they're helpful to me in that moment because they give me the illusion that I can do something about it. I can blame someone, or something, for what's happened, and I can anticipate the worst-case scenario and make plans to avoid it accordingly. These higher-energy emotions are also distracting me, and therefore protecting me, from feeling the more difficult lower-energy emotion of disappointment.

Is the answer to simply try and feel disappointment in these moments instead? Well, yes and no. I can honestly say I've never taken a moment, after failing an exam, to sit down and say to myself 'I feel really disappointed'. I have no doubt that if I had the presence of mind to do that in the moment, I might feel a little better somehow. But that's not real life. In real life, we often spiral into more active and seemingly more helpful emotions first and stay there.

What I *have* learnt to do, however, is to give my disappointment the space and time it needs to surface *shortly after* a disappointing event has occurred. Whether it's within a few minutes, hours or days, I give myself time to sit with my feelings of disappointment, to name them, and to share them with someone I trust.

By naming, feeling, and sharing our disappointment we're much less likely to get stuck in a cycle of distracting emotions like anger and fear. And much like grief, if we let our feelings of disappointment flow, they will diminish over time.

Stop for a moment and think. Is there something in your life that you're holding onto? Something you're feeling angry or scared about? Gently look at it again. Is there any element of disappointment that you haven't yet named and felt around this? Could you give yourself the permission and space you need to name and feel it now?

You may come to recognise many times in your life that you've felt disappointment and not given yourself permission to fully acknowledge it. The good news is that it's never too late to heal your feelings of disappointment. You just need to give yourself the time, space and permission to feel it.

16

Permission to be forgetful

"Man needs forgetfulness as well as memory."

James Stephens

Doctors and other healthcare professionals commonly worry about their memory. They describe forgetting the names of people they know, the names of drugs they use every day, or walking into a room and forgetting what it was they came in for. When they notice these things happening, they often jump to the worst-case conclusion in their heads. They worry that they have early-onset dementia or that their recent episode of ill health has left their memory permanently impaired.

The reality is these lapses in memory are common human experiences that happen to all of us from time to time. When you're used to your brain functioning at a very high level day-to-day, even the slightest dip can seem alarming. In very rare cases these subtle changes can herald the beginning of an underlying problem, but most cases can be explained by common factors such as stress, fatigue, hunger, rushing or simply being human.

Like most health-related symptoms, it can be helpful to think about the severity and impact of your forgetfulness.

If you're having the occasional memory lapse that isn't causing any major problems, it may be appropriate to wait and see if it gets better or worse over time. If you're forgetful to the extent that it impacts on your day-to-day life in a significant way, then you might need to speak to someone about it. Either way, it's always worth scanning for common causes of forgetfulness that can be reversed – like tiredness, busyness, hunger or stress.

For example, if you're busy at work one day and forget to have lunch, you don't necessarily need to consult a doctor about any memory lapses you have that afternoon. Simply set an alarm to remind you to have lunch the next day and try to protect your lunch break for the rest of the week. If, on the other hand, you miss lunch every day for a month because you 'forgot' to stop and eat because you weren't hungry, and you're losing weight, then you may want to talk this through with someone.

If you always forget the name of the same drug, or the same person, but you generally remember the names of other drugs and people in your life, then this is normal. If you're suddenly finding it hard to remember lots of people's names, or the names of lots of common drugs, then it might be worth getting your forgetfulness checked out.

Often all that's needed with forgetfulness is a gentle dose

of reassurance. We all forget why we walked into a room sometimes, and we all forget names and words occasionally too. It doesn't mean there's something wrong with our memory, it just means we're human.

Give yourself permission to forget sometimes. You can always ask someone or look things up if you need to.

Note: I once ran a poll on The Joyful Doctor Facebook page, asking doctors how often they had to look things up at work. Every respondent answered either 'several times a day' or 'several times a week'.

17

Permission to be obsessive and compulsive

*"Everyone has degrees of madness in them,
everyone has a story to tell."*

Bryony Gordon

I once knew a man with obsessive compulsive disorder (OCD) who couldn't write the letter 'H'. Every time he did, he was flooded with horrible intrusive thoughts that his wife would die.

In those moments, not writing the letter 'H' seemed like a small price to pay to save his wife's life. Over time, however, repeatedly giving in to his OCD like this meant he could never type the words 'Hi' or 'How are you?' in a text message or write 'Happy Birthday' or 'Thank you' in a card. His inability to write the letter 'H' started to ruin his close relationships and he couldn't hold down a job. His anxiety started to invade every aspect of his life, leaving him feeling tormented, depressed and alone.

With the help of a specialist therapist, a bit of time and a lot of courage, he was slowly able to start writing the letter 'H' again. He went from visibly shaking with fear every time he did so, to confidently sending messages with dozens of 'H's in them to all his friends, and his wife. He found a new job he loved and was able to move on with his life free from the torment of OCD.

I've lost count of the number of times I've heard someone describe themselves as 'a little bit OCD'. What they often fail to understand is how horrible OCD is, even in its mildest forms. It often seems that those who *don't* have it feel comfortable talking about it, while those who *do* have it want to keep it under wraps.

For OCD, the average length of time from onset of symptoms to diagnosis is twelve years.[12] I often diagnose and treat doctors who've been struggling with it for twenty years or more. OCD affects up to four percent of the population, and I suspect the incidence is much higher amongst doctors, who are prone to being perfectionistic by nature. Medicine is also a profession steeped in risk and responsibility: two factors that play a key role in maintaining the OCD cycle.

OCD is commonly minimised and misunderstood, even by mental health professionals. It was only when I spent three years working with the National OCD Service in London that I began to understand this condition for myself.

Like many others, I used to think OCD was just a bit of excessive handwashing or flicking the light switch on and off twenty times before you went to bed. I had no idea of the variety of different obsessions and compulsions OCD sufferers can experience, and that many of them are so steeped in shame and secrecy that they never speak them aloud.

Around one third of obsessive thoughts are sexual in nature; for example, thoughts about committing inappropriate sexual acts with others, including friends, pets or even children. In the most extreme cases, sufferers will have these thoughts several hundred times a day.

I've worked with sufferers who were so disgusted by these thoughts and frightened that they might act on them, that they voluntarily handed themselves into their local police station to keep others safe. They're not criminals though; they have OCD. They don't need punishment; they need treatment and support.

The intrusive thoughts of OCD are always repetitive and unpleasant. The sufferer will usually try to resist the thoughts in some way, at least to begin with. Most sufferers will also have compulsions – behaviours they feel they must or must not do.

Most sufferers have more than one type of intrusive thought and compulsion, and these can evolve and change over time. There will usually be a 'feared consequence' – a vague or specific fear of something bad happening to themselves or others – if they don't act on their intrusive thoughts and compulsions.

At the milder end, OCD can be quite subtle, and it can easily hide in plain sight. In its most severe forms, it can kill. For example, sufferers who have contamination fears relating to the use of toilets, can restrict their fluid intake to such dangerously low levels that they develop irreversible renal failure. Those who wash their hands so excessively that their skin breaks down and becomes infected, can be susceptible to life-threatening sepsis. Those tormented by particularly shameful or persistent intrusive thoughts can become very depressed and die by suicide.

There is a model of OCD that I often find helpful to share with my anxious doctor-patients: the Salkovskis' cognitive model of OCD.[13] Whether they have a formal diagnosis of OCD or not, I think it describes the day-to-day thoughts and behaviour patterns of anxious doctors perfectly.

The model starts by acknowledging the person's early life experiences. They were commonly anxious as a child or young adult. They often identify as being a perfectionist, a people-pleaser or someone who took responsibility for others from a young age.

They may have had some traumatic early life experiences or been prone to magical thinking growing up. They often went on to develop some strongly held beliefs, or rules for living, such as 'better safe than sorry' or 'I must do everything I can to prevent bad things from happening.'

The model continues by highlighting experiences later in life. The person will often describe a critical incident or triggering event. For example, a doctor might have missed the early warning signs of a treatable fatal condition in a patient who then dies. When this happens, their brain is flooded with completely natural and understandable thoughts such as, "This was my fault. I can't ever let this happen again." Most doctors would have intrusive thoughts like these for a few days or weeks. After a while, however, they usually settle, and they can go about their day-to-day working lives as before.

For those with OCD, however, it's a very different story. Their automatic negative thoughts take on a life of their own. They experience an even greater sense of responsibility and risk. They continue to feel entirely responsible for what has happened and try to do everything they can to reduce the risk of it happening again.

When the feared outcome is catastrophic, like a patient dying, even the smallest risk is intolerable. They need the risk of it happening again to be *zero*, however impossible this might be.

The model continues by showing that, in response to these increased feelings of risk and responsibility, a doctor with OCD will do one or more of the following four things:

Neutralising actions

They will try to reduce the risk of anything bad happening by engaging in neutralising actions. They might repeatedly run through what happened in their mind and do the same for future cases. They may constantly check to see if they have missed anything. They may stay late at work, checking notes and results until they feel safe.

They may find themselves obsessively worrying about patients when they're at home and even phone back into work to ask a colleague to check something for them. I've known many doctors do this, including me! They may take their laptop on holiday with them so they can keep checking that nothing bad has happened. They may repeatedly seek reassurance from the same colleague, or lots of different colleagues, until they feel sufficiently safe to move on.

Safety strategies

Doctors with OCD may try to keep safe by setting impossible criteria for themselves or others. For example, they may run every test twice before making any clinical decisions, or expect their junior colleagues to cover new cases in impossible detail. They may try to minimise any risk or responsibility by avoiding seeing certain patients or taking time off work. They may try to push their anxious thoughts out of their head, and when this doesn't work, turn to alcohol, drugs, or other unhealthy distractions to cope.

Attentional bias

Those with OCD or OCD-like anxiety may start to focus their attention on certain things; for example, scanning their daily patient list for high-risk patients. This is commonly referred to as 'looking for trouble'. It gives the doctor the illusion that they can avoid trouble completely, or be more prepared for it when it does come along.

Mood changes

Finally, those with OCD commonly experience changes in their mood, becoming increasingly distressed, anxious or depressed over time.

In the short-term these four responses – neutralising actions, safety behaviours, attentional bias and mood changes – are designed to reduce anxiety. However, in the long-term they make things worse. For example, seeking reassurance may help a doctor feel less anxious right now, but the next time a patient comes along with the same symptoms, the whole cycle begins over again.

Avoidance may seem like a great way to reduce anxiety in the short-term, but it makes it harder to face the same situation in the future. Looking for trouble may give them the illusion that they can avoid trouble, or be more prepared for it when it comes along, but it also keeps them trapped in a state of hyperarousal and threat.

It may sound bizarre to suggest that feeling anxious or depressed is your brain's way of trying to *reduce* your anxiety, but it is. Anxiety is a state of heightened arousal which makes you feel more ready for action. Worrying about something makes your brain think that you're 'doing something about it'.

Becoming depressed, on the other hand, helps you to

retreat and avoid, meaning you don't have to face the feared situation. However, in the long run, both anxiety and depression continue to feed the OCD cycle and make the situation worse.

If you identify with any of these behaviours, the good news is, there are lots of things you can do to help reduce them. By targeting any point of the OCD cycle you can improve things for yourself.

For example, you could gradually stop avoiding certain tasks and allow yourself to check things only once. You could stop looking for trouble and focus more on what's going well instead. You could challenge your degree of responsibility in any given situation and correct your overestimation of the risks involved.

You could reduce your anxiety or improve your mood through exercise, meditation or doing something fun. Anything you do to gently reverse the OCD cycle will help.

Whatever you choose to do, my number one tip is this: *don't try to do it on your own.*

Give yourself permission to get some help. Over time, you can learn to 'be your own therapist' but, to start with at least, it's much easier to recover with some support and professional guidance.

You may want to read a reputable self-help book, look at national OCD websites, find a good therapist, take medication or join a support group.

Obsessions and compulsions can be sneaky little

things. You might need help to learn what is the OCD-way and what is the anti-OCD way of doing things. It will take time, courage and practice, and you'll have to face your fears, but you can absolutely do it like many have before you.

Like the patient I knew who couldn't write the letter 'H', you can learn to manage your obsessions and compulsions and get your life back again.

18

Permission to feel traumatised

"There is no greater agony than
carrying an untold story inside you."

Maya Angelou

Trauma is our response to any event we find physically or emotionally threatening, or harmful to ourselves or others. Many doctors carry traumatic memories inside them. It's almost impossible to get through medical school, and to work as a doctor, without being exposed to multiple traumatic events.

Doctors can be directly affected by trauma. For example, the GP I treated who was stalked and sexually assaulted by a patient in her consultation room, or the paediatric trainee who watched on helplessly as a newborn baby died in front of her.

Doctors can be traumatised indirectly, by hearing or reading about their patients' traumas, or by witnessing traumatic events happening to others. They can also be traumatised by the ill health of their loved ones. For example, the GP I treated who cared for her elderly father dying from dementia, or the young hospital doctor who had to resuscitate her husband after he had a sudden cardiac arrest.

Many doctors carry traumatic memories from undertaking 'Good Samaritan' acts on planes, or by the roadside. And too many have been traumatised by discovering the body of a colleague, who has died by suicide in the workplace.

In addition to all these medically-related traumas, doctors can also experience the same traumatic life experiences as anyone else, such as sexual abuse, domestic violence, life-threatening accidents, natural disasters and war.

Traumatic events are a normal and common part of human life. Most people who experience a significant traumatic event will have what we call a 'normal stress response'. In the days and weeks immediately following the event, they'll find themselves preoccupied with frequent intrusive images and thoughts about what happened popping into their mind. They may feel more on edge than usual and have trouble sleeping or relaxing.

For most people, including doctors, these symptoms will typically resolve over two to six weeks. However, after a significant traumatic event, approximately one third of people will experience a more severe or persistent pattern of symptoms, developing a condition called Post-Traumatic Stress Disorder (PTSD).

PTSD is made up of three main symptom clusters. The first is *reliving experiences*, for example, flashbacks or nightmares. These may be obvious, like the incident flashing in front of your eyes, or more subtle, like a momentary taste in your mouth or a sensation in your body.

The second symptom cluster is *hyperarousal*; for example, feeling on edge or having trouble sleeping. You may find yourself sensing danger around every corner and jumping through the roof at the smallest sound.

The third symptom cluster is *avoidance*; for example, trying to push the memory out of your mind, avoiding anything that reminds you of what happened, or turning to drugs or alcohol to block the memory out.

The symptoms of trauma can range from distressing but manageable, to being so severe that the person is unable to function day-to-day. Trauma symptoms are frequently mislabelled by the sufferer or others as something else, such as anxiety, agoraphobia or depression.

I often treat doctors who have PTSD but don't realise it. They may be misattributing their insomnia to 'always being a bad sleeper', or avoiding working in a certain speciality without realising why. They may be drinking more than usual or spending more time on their own. Most often, I see doctors keeping busy, throwing themselves into work to distract them from the horrible trauma symptoms that surface when they try to relax.

The good news is that PTSD responds well to a number of different talking therapies, for example trauma-focused CBT (Cognitive Behavioural Therapy) or EMDR (Eye Movement Desensitisation and Reprocessing). These treatments are not easy to go through, but they are well worth trying because they can give you your life back.

I've had PTSD twice in my life and both times it's responded well to talking therapy. The first time I had therapy was to deal with some traumatic memories from my childhood. Around the age of eight I was groomed and sexually assaulted by an eighteen-year-old man.

I remember driving to my first therapy sessions as an adult feeling terrified of what I was about to face. My hands gripped the steering wheel so tightly that my knuckles turned white. Every fibre of my being wanted to turn the car around and go home. I couldn't bear the thought of reliving what had happened. I just wanted to avoid it, get rid of it and forget about it. But I knew I had to face it, and I trusted my therapist when he told me that I would feel better if I did.

Just a few sessions later, when the treatment started to work, it felt as if someone had flicked off a switch. It was a surreal experience. For the first time in nearly thirty years, I felt completely calm and safe. I no longer walked down the street expecting something bad to happen. I could remember the traumatic things that had happened to me without having to relive them.

I chose to report my history of assault to the police and received some very helpful support from their victim support service. The police were able to confirm that the perpetrator was already in prison having committed several other similar offences against underage girls.

I started to talk about what had happened to me with my close friends and family. I no longer felt ashamed. I could move on with my life. I was free.

A decade later, after years of living free from my trauma symptoms, I had a near-miss car accident. Another car nearly collided with mine on a roundabout, and for a split second I thought I was going to die. My neck and back went into spasm. Over the next few weeks, I started to notice my startle response increasing again. The slightest surprise made me jump out of my skin and it was taking longer and longer for me to calm down each time.

I decided to get in touch with my trauma therapist again and we arranged to do some more sessions of EMDR. We started working on the traumatic memory of my recent car accident, but it quickly became clear that this wasn't the main memory causing me problems.

The car accident had re-triggered the memory of when I was mugged at knifepoint as a medical student in Boston a few years before. My mind and body were treating both events the same. In both situations – the mugging and the subsequent car accident – the threat had come at me suddenly from the left-hand side of my body. And in each moment, I thought I was going to die.

As my therapy sessions continued it became clear that the trauma of the mugging was also closely linked to some other experiences I'd had as a medical student and junior doctor. With the benefit of hindsight this link was blindingly obvious. I was mugged in my final year of medical school, and a few months later, with my undiagnosed PTSD in full swing, I started my first job on the wards as a junior doctor. In both situations, being mugged and working on the wards, I felt dangerously out of my depth, out of control, and afraid for my life and the lives of others.

My therapist and I patiently worked through the memory of the mugging together, and then several subsequent traumatic memories as they came up. After a few more sessions our perseverance started to pay off. My neck and back began to release tension I'd unknowingly held onto since the day I was mugged. And I managed to heal the remaining traumatic memories from my years as a medical student and junior doctor.

I think of those of us who've had PTSD as having a 'vulnerable brain' when it comes to trauma. When we experience another traumatic event, we may have an exaggerated stress response. Our 'normal stress response' may feel more intense or last a bit longer than it does for others. We need to watch out for signs of PTSD relapse and give ourselves permission to seek help early if we notice any.

I often tell my patients that facing their trauma may be the hardest things they ever do, but it will improve their lives immeasurably. We plan the sessions carefully, including any time off work they may need for the appointments or for the duration of the therapy. I reassure them that, while they may dread coming to the sessions at first, it will be OK. I will be with them every step of the way, and the freedom they gain from their traumatic memories will be worth every painful moment it takes to get there.

When doctors come to me for trauma therapy, I usually share two or three metaphors with them to help them understand their trauma symptoms and how the treatment is going to work. I'd like to share these metaphors with you too. I hope they may help you to understand any traumatic memories you may be carrying, or those affecting others you know.

The filing cabinet

There are two parts of the brain that play a key role in laying down trauma memories: the amygdala, the 'emotion centre', and the hippocampus, the 'filing cabinet'. When something ordinary and uneventful happens in your day-to-day life, your amygdala, the emotion centre, remains calm and quiet. This allows your brain to neatly store the memory of what has happened in the filing cabinet of your brain, the hippocampus.

For example, when you had breakfast this morning, chances are that nothing too traumatic happened. Your amygdala will have stayed calm and your hippocampus will have stored the memory away quite neatly.

If I asked you to remember what you'd eaten for breakfast this morning, your brain would go to its hippocampus, search under 'breakfast' and today's date, and pull out the relevant file. You'd then be able to tell me, for example, that you ate a bowl of cereal and drank a cup of tea. Your amygdala would remain calm and all would be well.

Now let's imagine a different scenario. Imagine that, as you were eating breakfast this morning, someone with a gun burst into your home and threatened to kill you. In this situation, your brain's emotion centre, the amygdala, would go berserk. This would send your hippocampus into panic mode. It would start shoving the memory into the filing cabinet as quickly as possible, dropping some of the memory on the floor, and cramming the rest of it in wherever it could.

The chaos of it all would make it hard for your brain to shut the filing cabinet door. As you continued about your day-to-day life, over the coming weeks and months, the memory of what had happened would keep spilling out of the cabinet, intruding into your mind without warning.

When I asked you to recall what happened that day, you might find chunks of the memory still missing, and other parts firmly imprinted on your brain. What you saw, thought, smelt, tasted and heard may be all jumbled up and stored in different parts of your brain's filing cabinet, alongside other memories that might not seem related at all.

When something reminds you of what happened, your amygdala, the emotion centre of your brain, would spring back into overdrive and you could stay stuck there for days.

Trauma therapy can help by gently piecing back together the different parts of the memory. It's like pulling out the messy parts of the memory from the filing cabinet and sorting it into a sensible order. You can then neatly file the memory away again in the right section of the filing cabinet, gently shut the door and walk away.

You'll always have that memory, and you can think about it any time you want to, but it won't intrude on your life as it used to. When you do think about it, your amygdala will stay much calmer than before. You will be able to remember what happened without reliving it.

The dirty duvet

Having an untreated trauma memory can also be like owning a really dirty duvet that's stinking your whole house out. Imagine you are at home one day and your phone rings. It's a favourite relative saying they are going to pop over to visit you in the next few minutes. You put the phone down and start to panic. You really want to see them, but you have this stinky old duvet, making your whole house smell bad, and you don't know what to do with it.

You don't have time to wash the duvet before your relative arrives, so you decide to grab it and shove it into a nearby cupboard. The problem is that it's too big and it won't fit. You frantically push and squeeze at it, cramming it in as best you can. Then you have to stand with your back pressed against the cupboard door to keep it from spilling out.

That's what it feels like when your brain is trying to keep a traumatic memory at bay. You're working hard, day and night, to stop the stinking memory from crashing into your mind. You can't let up for a moment or it will overwhelm you and stink your whole life out. You feel trapped, miserable and exhausted, and you're using up all your energy to keep the memory at bay. You can't enjoy your relative's visit because you're stuck standing with your back against the cupboard door.

When I share this metaphor with doctors suffering from severe PTSD, they invariably say: "That's exactly how it feels." They're exhausted from months or years of keeping their back pressed against the cupboard door and they can't see any other way out. Their traumatic memories are so horrible, so scary, so repellent that the thought of opening the door and getting the memory out deliberately is unthinkable.

I go on to explain, that when we do trauma therapy, it's as if I'm standing there with them, next to that cupboard door. I explain that I'm an expert at cleaning duvets and I'm going to help them clean theirs.

I prepare them fully for what we're going to do, telling them about every step of the duvet cleaning process before we get started. I reassure them that they'll remain in control the whole time and they can pause and take breaks whenever they need to.

I explain that, when they're ready, I'll help them to slowly step away from the cupboard door. Then we'll grab the dirty duvet together and shove it in the washing machine. I warn them that this part of the process can be pretty tough because we have to be with the stinky duvet for a while, but it usually only takes one or two sessions before we can shove the duvet in the washing machine and shut the door on it. At this point things will start to feel a lot better.

When we take the duvet out of the washing machine it will smell and look a whole lot nicer than it did before. It may still have the odd stain on it, but we can use a bit of stain remover and put it through a quick rinse cycle. Then it will be fully cleaned. Finally, we can dry the duvet out, fold it up neatly and gently place it back in the cupboard. At this point they'll be able to peacefully shut the door and walk away.

They'll always have that trauma memory, the duvet, but now it will be stored in their brain in a much nicer, calmer way. They can choose to look at it whenever they want to, and when they do, it will look and smell nicer than it did before. If, one day in the future, something triggers the memory of that 'dirty duvet', they'll be able to remember how it *used* to smell and feel, and be grateful that it won't ever smell and feel that bad again.

The domino effect

Many people carry more than one traumatic memory from their lifetime. It's not unusual for one person to carry fifteen or more traumatic memories in their mind. This doesn't necessarily alter how we approach the treatment or how effective it can be.

In this situation we simply map out the different memories and measure how much distress each one is causing them in the current day. Together, we can then choose what we call the 'domino memory'. This is usually one of the earliest and most disturbing memories that links to their more recent and disturbing memories in some way.

If we heal this earlier memory first, all the subsequent memories tend to improve as well. Like pushing over the first domino in a domino run. All the effort goes into pushing over that first memory, then the rest simply fall into place. For most people, working on just one memory is enough to significantly improve their PTSD symptoms. Occasionally we need to work with a second or third memory, but this is often quicker and easier to do after the first memory has improved.

The way different therapists work with traumatic memories varies depending on the model of therapy they use. I tend to use trauma-focused CBT which has three stages. First, we prepare for the work by setting the scene, exploring the metaphors, and practising some grounding exercises the person can use if they need to as the therapy progresses.

Next, we have the 'active' treatment phase in which the person relives their domino memory, by talking it through slowly, as if it were happening to them now. Then we talk through the memory again together in detail, deciding whether to update it or rescript it, or a combination of both.

Updating is when we use new information that the person didn't have at the time to update the memory. For example, if they were in a serious car accident and thought they were going to die, we can update the memory with the information that they didn't die.

Rescripting is a useful alternative when it's not possible to update the memory in this way. For example, I once worked with a medical student who was sexually assaulted on a bus. She couldn't update the memory with a positive outcome, because there wasn't one. Instead, she chose to rescript the ending of the memory.

She imagined an ending where the police came and arrested the perpetrator and he ended up in prison. This new ending helped her to process her natural anger towards the perpetrator and satisfied her desire for justice to be done. From that point forward, she couldn't remember what had happened without imaging the new ending and enjoying the feelings of relief and safety it brought.

Rescripting can be realistic in nature or completely fantastical. You don't need to believe that the new rescripted version of events actually happened for it to work. We simply trust your brain to reimagine what happened in whatever way it needs or wants to.

We also work together at this stage to correct any unhelpful beliefs, for example, "It was my fault", and answer any unanswered questions, such as "Why did this happen to me?"

By the time we've updated and rescripted the memory, and addressed any unhelpful beliefs, most of the trauma symptoms will have improved. The memory will be far less distressing to recall. If any other memories are still causing significant distress, we can repeat the process above with those memories too.

After this second active phase of treatment, we move onto the final and nicest phase of trauma therapy: *reclaiming your life*. This is when you start to trust that your trauma symptoms have really improved, and you begin to reclaim the parts of your life that you lost to being traumatised.

I love this part of the process because this is when I get to watch my doctor-patients moving on with their lives, free from their PTSD symptoms. They rediscover lost hobbies and interests, embark on new relationships and take courageous steps forward in their personal and professional lives.

They start to let go of their old unhelpful survival strategies and give themselves permission to really enjoy their lives again. This can feel very strange and unfamiliar to them at first. It can feel as if nothing has changed, but everything has changed, all at the same time.

Gradually, over the course of the next twelve to eighteen months, they slowly learn to trust this new trauma-free way of living and eventually it becomes their 'new normal'. Their trauma becomes something they talk about in the past tense and can even sometimes forget.

If you're wondering if you may be affected by carrying untreated trauma memories inside you, then please give yourself permission to get some help. It may feel very scary – that's completely normal – but it could also be the best thing you ever do.

You don't have to keep standing there with your back pressed against the cupboard door. With help, and a little time, you can clean that dirty duvet and move on with your life.

Note: There's a form of PTSD called Complex PTSD (CPTSD) which occurs when a person is exposed to multiple traumatic experiences over a prolonged period of time. CPTSD can also respond well to trauma-focused therapies but may require a more protracted course of treatment and support over many months or years. Even with this more complex and challenging diagnosis, there's still hope; you can heal and gain a better quality of life over time.

19

Permission to bleed

"I would like to cancel my monthly subscription."

Biologically Female Anon

I stood at the side of the pool and reached for my towel. I planned to wrap its cosy warm fibres around me and float over to the changing rooms to indulge in a blissful, long, hot shower. It was going to be the perfect end to the perfect day.

I'd spent the last few hours at a luxurious spa with two of my closest friends. We'd whiled away the hours talking, relaxing, daydreaming, swimming and breathing, unencumbered by the stresses of our everyday lives. The beautiful autumn sun shone through the floor-to-ceiling windows, bathing the pool in an intoxicating warm light. I felt as if I'd spent the day in heaven.

As I reached for my fluffy, white, oversized towel, I looked down and noticed there was something different about the floor by my feet.

It took me a few moments to realise what was

different. It was pink. At first, I thought the autumn light must be dancing on the small pool of water by my feet, but the water kept getting pinker and pinker, and now it was almost red.

I noticed the red colour was densest near my right ankle. I traced it upwards into a line that ran across the front of my ankle and up the inside of my lower leg. My eyes continued scanning upwards, up and over my knee and onwards up the inside of my thigh. Then I realised what was happening. This was my period. And I was bleeding. A lot.

I panicked.

My body went into fight, flight and freeze mode.

"What do I do?" I thought urgently. "If I stop here, it'll get worse. If I move, I'll trail blood along with me. This is a public place, there's water everywhere. This is going to be a blood bath…literally."

There were people all around the pool, but my friends were nowhere in sight. I had to do something.

I chose what seemed to be the lesser of two evils between stopping still and moving: I moved. I quickly wrapped the towel around me, wedging a little of it awkwardly between my legs to stem the flow of blood. I waddled, like a bow-legged penguin, as fast as I could to the changing room showers.

Once there, I stood, letting the water from the shower wash away my blood and embarrassment as I tried to figure out my next move. My face flushed, breathing hard, feeling mortified and angry, I started to rant to myself.

"Why did this have to happen to me? Why now? Why

today?"

You might be thinking that my period took me by surprise that day, but it didn't.

I knew I had my period that day and I was well prepared. I was expecting the last of my tampons to last me until well after my return home, just two hours later. Unfortunately, my body hadn't got that memo, and I was now flooding in a shower cubicle with no help in sight.

Flooding is what happens when a woman's body suddenly, and often unexpectedly, releases an unusually high volume of menstrual blood in a short space of time. In its most severe form, it can be extremely distressing and cause secondary problems like nausea, fainting, and collapse. I'd never experienced flooding to this degree before, and I don't mind admitting it scared me.

As a doctor I know how to estimate blood loss just by looking at it. I know it often looks worse than it is. It can be especially misleading when mixed with running water. Even so, I could see that I was losing a lot of blood, and I was on my own in a shower cubicle, struggling to think straight about what to do next.

Leaning on the shower cubicle wall to brace myself from the abdominal cramps that had started, I was beginning to feel quite faint. I knew this was most likely due to the anxiety of the situation, not the blood loss itself, but either way it didn't feel good.

I heard the distant voices of my friends as they came into the changing room chatting, blissfully unaware of my bloody predicament.

"Help... I'm flooding!" I shouted, unable to form a more coherent sentence.

"I don't have anything!" one of my friends replied apologetically.

"Me neither," the other chimed in, the empathy palpable in her voice.

"There's a machine by the sinks!" I blurted, before an alarming gush of blood took my breath away.

"I don't have any money... but I have coins in the car!" the first friend replied.

"Thank you... so sorry... thank you..." I said, aware that I was struggling to talk through the toxic combination of pain, fear, blood loss, and embarrassment.

I needed to sit down. I was feeling increasingly weak and starting to think I might faint.

I grabbed my towel, acutely aware of how awful it looked, blood-stained and all. Safe in the relatively accepting environment of a female changing room, I elected for practicality over modesty and shoved the whole thing between my legs. Waddling like an even more bow-legged penguin this time, I made my way to my locker and started searching frantically for anything that could help me, while my friend dressed quickly and went to get coins from her car for the tampon machine.

My locker was bare. I started to feel desperate. I looked around me, searching for anything that might help. As I turned, there was a woman standing just a few feet away. I grimaced at her with a mixture of hope and embarrassment. She looked down at my feet. I looked down at the floor. Our eyes were met with a growing pool of bright red blood.

"I'm so sorry," I said. I felt bad that she should have to see this awful sight.

"Please don't worry," she replied kindly. "It's happened to all of us."

We both glanced expectantly over at a third women in the changing room who'd witnessed this compassionate exchange of sisterhood. She was older than us both. She smiled kindly and said apologetically and knowingly: "I don't miss that."

A fourth kind stranger came over to us and passed me a tiny panty-liner, not much bigger than a tissue, apologetically saying: "This is all I have, I hope it helps."

I politely wedged it between my crotch and the oversized towel that, by this stage, had given up hope of ever being called white again, and I thanked her. Even if the panty-liner was woefully inadequate for the job, the gesture meant more to me than she would ever know.

My thoughts started to swirl uncontrollably in my head.

"I have to do something... there's blood by my feet... there's blood by the pool... this is a health and safety risk... not to mention disgusting... these poor people... they're just trying to relax and now they're surrounded by my blood..."

I waddled to the changing room door, which was thankfully just opposite the spa reception desk. I opened the door a couple of inches and signalled with my eyes to the female staff member sitting at reception. The shame and embarrassment of the situation was oozing from every pore by now and she knew to come straight over.

"I'm so sorry... I've started bleeding suddenly. There's some blood by the side of the pool..."

"Are you OK?" she asked kindly.

"Yes, I'm fine," I replied in an overly chirpy tone. "My friend is bringing me something. It's just the blood... It'll need to be cleaned up... I can't do it, I'm still bleeding... I'm so sorry."

I explained where she should look, as if the trail of blood along the floor wouldn't be a big enough clue. Then I shuffled, with my towel-tail between my legs, back to my locker to wait for my friend to rescue me.

"I'm fine."

I heard myself saying those words in my head and I couldn't quite believe it.

"Why the hell did I tell her I'm fine? I'm obviously not fine!"

The truth was, in that moment I was far from fine. I was shocked and embarrassed. I felt weak and scared. I was feeling light-headed and not sure what to do next. I needed help and was most certainly not fine.

As I stood, still bleeding heavily, berating myself for hiding my needs behind a veil of shame and politeness, my friend appeared like a fairy godmother with a collection of coins in her hand. She hurried to feed the machine of eternal hope.

Relief coursed through my veins as I anticipated the imminent return of control over Mother Nature. Although

"Why should I feel embarrassed about this? Why has my culture conditioned me to feel shame about a completely normal human process that's outside of my control? I don't feel ashamed when I sneeze or breathe, so why should I feel ashamed when I bleed? Why should something that happens to half of the world's population, for half of their life, be shrouded in such secrecy, stigma and shame? Why?"

I know that many wonderful books, podcasts, blogs, and documentaries have tried to answer these very important questions. I'm hopeful that these are not questions that women born a hundred years from now will still have to battle with quite so intensely.

For now, I'll just share this.

I made a conscious choice in that moment. I decided I wouldn't shout from the rooftops about what had happened to me that day, but I wouldn't hide it away either. I decided I'd talk to my friends, both male and female, about the experience I'd had, and I'd get the identification and support I needed.

I also decided to add a chapter to this book, and instead of calling it 'Permission to feel embarrassed', I decided to call it 'Permission to bleed'.

20

Permission to feel happy

*"Cry. Forgive. Learn. Move on. Let your tears
water the seeds of your future happiness."*

Steve Marabol

One winter's day, in my late twenties, I found myself in a supermarket staring at an artificial Christmas tree. It was six-foot tall, standing proudly decorated in front of all the other boxed-up Christmas trees. Christmas music was being piped into the air around me, but all I could hear was silence, and all I could sense was this tree and a strange physical sensation building up behind my eyes.

It felt like hundreds of tiny electrical synapses bursting into life, followed by a pleasant breeze clearing the fog in my brain from front to back. I felt my eyes widen and the corners of my mouth lift to meet them. It felt so strange and so wonderful, and it took me a few moments to realise what was happening.

I was smiling.

The pleasant feeling continued to spread throughout my head and body. My chin lifted slightly and I felt my lungs fill with air. My shoulders eased backwards and my arms and legs felt loose and light. I had energy. I felt alive. I felt happy. Not the fake kind of happiness I'd been putting on for show lately, but a genuine, warm and glowing happiness that came from somewhere deep inside me.

I was bewildered and surprised. I couldn't remember the last time I'd felt like this. It felt familiar and yet brand new at the same time. I was scared that if I moved an inch the happiness might disappear, leaving me just as suddenly as it had found me again. And so, I stood, suspended in a precarious and precious moment of joy, just me and the Christmas tree.

"Caroline, are you OK?"

My two friends were next to me, showing quiet concern.

I woke from my happy moment, turned to them and spoke.

"I'm OK... I'm... happy..." I said, with tears building behind my eyes.

My friends knew the significance of this moment, as did I. They stood with me in silence for a few more moments, as I continued to beam happiness at that tree.

My two good friends from medical school had come to stay for the weekend. When I called to suggest they cancel their visit, because I was depressed, they said: "No way, we're still coming."

So here they were, standing next to me, offering no judgement, just time. I sensed them both waiting patiently until I felt ready to talk again.

When I started to trust that my words wouldn't frighten the good feelings away, I explained what was happening inside me.

"I feel happy," I said. "Really happy. I just saw this tree and I started to feel happy... I used to love Christmas. I've always loved Christmas, but this year felt different. I wasn't looking forward to it and I didn't know why. I've been desperate to love Christmas again and I couldn't make it happen. I've walked past these trees a dozen times in the past few weeks and felt nothing, just dead inside, and now... I feel happy."

I paused and looked at my friends and they looked back at me.

"Right, we're buying this tree!" one of them said, and we all burst out laughing.

We'd only gone to the supermarket to pick up some dinner, so we hadn't brought the car with us. Despite this, my friends insisted that we buy the Christmas tree, and they helped me carry it all the way home. We put it up, decorated it together, and basked in the shared festive spirit for a while.

Later that evening, as my depression claimed my thoughts once more, and I sat on the sofa bleak and despairing, my friends kept the memory of my happiness alive until I was ready to feel it again.

In the days and weeks that followed, I experienced

more and more moments of happiness and hope. My happy feelings came more frequently and lasted for longer. I started to trust that I'd make it through the darkness. I also experienced something I'd never felt before: I felt bad about feeling good. Feeling happy suddenly came with an unpleasant side helping of guilt.

Each time I felt happy, I immediately thought I should go back to work. After all, how could I be off sick from work with depression if I was now able to laugh and smile and feel happy again?

"If I can feel good in this moment, I must be well enough to work," I thought. "What if someone from work sees me out and about smiling and thinks I'm well? What if they think I'm faking being ill and I'm just having a good time?"

I didn't give myself permission to be happy and off work at the same time. I had, what I now call, *happiness-guilt*.

I regularly hear doctors describe happiness-guilt as they start to recover from mental health conditions. At the first sign of improvement, they start thinking about when they can go back to work. They think that having one good day means they're ready to return, but it doesn't.

Anyone who's ever broken a leg may tell a similar tale. The first steps you take unaided by crutches can be scary and weird, yet strangely familiar and full of hope. Immediately your brain races ahead, planning your triumphant return to 'walking normally'. You may even call up your jogging buddy and start planning your next charity run. Unfortunately, Mother Nature has different ideas, and having pushed things too quickly, you can easily find yourself back on crutches for the rest of the week.

The same thing happens with mental health recovery. We often take two steps forward and one step back. And sometimes we take one step forward and two steps back. We're constantly under- and over-estimating the daily needs of our minds and bodies. We make mistakes and have to constantly readjust our expectations of what's possible and realistic.

When we break a leg, it's not until we can repeatedly walk a fair distance unaided that we should consider gently jogging again. When we're recovering from a mental health condition like depression or burnout, it's not until we're consistently happy on most days of the week, for at least a couple of weeks, that we should start to plan our next steps on the recovery journey, like returning to work. With both physical and mental illnesses, it's important to build up our stamina and resilience before forging ahead.

This predictably unpredictable path of recovery means that we'll have many happy moments, days even, while still off sick from work with mental health problems. The ebbs and flows of recovery will continue once we return to work as well, as we continue to have good and bad days. This is all part of the normal recovery process from mental and physical health conditions.

For now, please remember this: you have permission to be happy when you're off sick from work – for a moment, a few hours, a day or even longer. It's OK.

Another time we experience happiness-guilt is when the people we care about aren't happy. Doctors often experience this when they're having a good day but the patient in front of them is not.

When those around us are in pain, struggling, grieving, anxious or low, we can easily feel a sense of guilt if our own emotions are more positive. This is perfectly normal. Feeling happy when others are not doesn't mean we don't care, or that we're a bad person, it just means we're happy.

I also see happiness-guilt surface when a natural disaster or world conflict is filling the twenty-four-hour news cycle. Many a happy day has been hijacked by a quick scroll of the headlines on my phone or a few minutes watching the news.

I still remember the strange and incongruent feeling of attending an international opera performance, as a medical student in Edinburgh, just a few hours after the 9/11 terrorist attacks happened in New York and Washington. After much debating, my friends and I decided that we should still go to the performance.

We wanted to honour those suffering in the United States and around the world, by not taking our freedom and relative safety for granted. We wanted to relish and appreciate every precious moment and opportunity in life. We also wanted to show up for the performers – who had no choice but for the 'show to go on'.

We didn't feel exactly happy that night, but we'd

given ourselves permission to let our good and bad feelings exist alongside each other. I have often thought since, that this is the secret to living a more joyful life.

You may find happiness brings you feelings of anxiety rather than guilt. When you start to feel happy you may find you start to worry about losing that feeling. Professor Brené Brown has given a name to this anticipatory anxiety in the face of happy emotions. She calls it 'foreboding joy'.[14] This is a sense that your happiness can't last; that you're waiting for something bad to happen, for the other shoe to drop.

You may also feel mistrustful of your happy feelings and question whether they are real feelings at all. You may think your brain is playing tricks on you and that your happy feelings are just an illusion. Then, when your happy feelings do pass, as all feelings do, you may take this as confirmatory evidence that they were never real in the first place.

The antidote to both foreboding joy and mistrusting your happy feelings is to practice *gratitude*. If you can drop into gratitude during your moments of happiness, your happy feelings are much less likely to be hijacked by feelings of mistrust and fear. Over time, with repeated gratitude practice, you'll start to trust and enjoy your feelings of happiness more.

21

Permission to feel grateful

"Gratitude is riches. Complaint is poverty."

Doris Day

Gratitude is like a magic drug. You can take it regularly to keep you healthy, or as needed when the going gets tough. Gratitude eases almost all emotional pain and you can't overdose on it. It's difficult to feel gratitude and to simultaneously feel sadness, anger, regret, fear, or other challenging emotions. Building a regular gratitude practice into your life can completely transform your outlook and emotional wellbeing.

To build your own regular gratitude practice simply try out different ways of bringing gratitude into your life and keep repeating the ways that work for you. Much like you would have different tools in a toolbox for different jobs around the house, you'll need different ways to bring gratitude into your day. You'll need some everyday gratitude tools, as well a couple of specialist tools for any particularly tough moments.

In a moment I'll list a few ways to practice gratitude that you might like to try. But before I do this, I want to make a really important point about gratitude that you need to keep in mind. When you practice gratitude, it's important that you don't *just list* the things you feel grateful for.

I could rattle off a list of things I'm grateful for right now, such as having a roof over my head, food on my plate, and a loving relationship. Simply listing these things doesn't make me *feel* grateful. It's just a list. To feel the full benefit of gratitude we must think about *why* those things make us feel grateful. That's when the magic happens.

Try this for yourself now. Think of one thing you are grateful for right now. Now think about *why* you're grateful for it. Think about what it means to you, why it's important, how it helps you, or what it would be like not to have that thing in your life. See the difference? To experience the full power of gratitude you must really feel it. This is why, in all the examples of gratitude practices I'm about to list, I've suggested you say, write, or share what you're grateful for and *why*.

Here are a few suggestions on how to practice gratitude in your life:

Gratitude lists

- Set a timer for three minutes and write down a list of all the things you're grateful for and why.

- First thing in the morning or last thing at night, write down three things you are grateful for and why.

- As you brush your teeth or hair each day, think of three things you are grateful for and why.

It's important when using gratitude lists regularly that you try to think of different things you're grateful for each time you make a list. If you list the same things each time, your brain and body will soon switch off from connecting with the deeper feelings of gratitude and revert to simply listing them as items.

If you do want to repeat something – for example, you feel grateful for the same person in your life today as yesterday – then try to think of a different reason why you feel grateful for them. For example, you may be grateful for your partner one day because they make you laugh, and the next day because they listen to you.

Other gratitude practices

- Keep a gratitude jar or box. Set a timer for ten minutes and write down everything you're grateful for, and why, on separate pieces of paper. Put them in your jar / box. When you're having a tough day, pick one out and reflect on it for a moment. Each time something good happens, add it to your collection.

- Use a gratitude app on your phone – there are many great free ones out there. Use the app to document your gratitude in words or photos, or to send you reminders to pause for a moment and think of something you feel grateful for.

- If you like writing, consider keeping a gratitude journal in which you can regularly write about the things you're grateful for in more depth. Set a regular date with yourself, your gratitude journal and your favourite cup of tea or coffee.

- Keep a voice journal on your phone. Record yourself talking about what you're grateful for. When you're having a bad day, pick a recording at random and listen to it.

- Write or read a poem or prayer about gratitude. Collect and memorise one or two favourite pieces. Keep them by your bedside or on your desk at work and revisit them daily, or save them on your phone to access them on-the-go when you need them.

- Try a gratitude meditation. Set a timer for a few minutes and sit quietly contemplating something you feel grateful for. Each time your mind wanders, gently guide your focus back to the person or thing you feel grateful for.

Shared gratitude

The power of gratitude magnifies when you share it with others. Why not try one of the following simple ways to share gratitude with those you love?

- With your partner or children, when sitting down to breakfast or dinner, or driving to and from work or school, take it in turns to share something you're grateful for that happened that day or the day before. Don't forget to share *why* you feel grateful for it to feel the full benefit.

- With your work colleagues, begin or end your meetings by sharing one thing you're each grateful for, and why.

- With a friend, each time you meet for coffee or chat on the phone, start or end your conversation by sharing something you each feel grateful for and why.

- Start your working week by sending a brief email or message to a colleague, sharing your gratitude for something they did or said recently.

- Spend time with your family or work colleagues creating a shared gratitude jar, tin or box, that you can all dip into when you need a little boost.

Stealth gratitude

It's also fun to see if you can share gratitude with others without them noticing. Try slipping some gratitude into a conversation with someone today and notice what happens.

Emergency gratitude

Here are some suggestions for bringing gratitude into your life during difficult moments and tough times.

- Reach into your personal or family gratitude jar, tin or box and pull out a little gratitude memory. Spend a few moments enjoying the memory.

- Look around the room and name one thing you can see, hear or touch that you are grateful for. Think about *why* you are grateful for it.

- List three things you are grateful for in this moment and why.

- Think about the last time you felt grateful for something and focus on *why* it made you feel grateful.

- Ask someone else what they are feeling grateful for right now, and why.

- Mark this page in the book to come back to when you're having a bad day.

Gratitude is an often-underestimated feeling. It has the power to transform your life for the better. Give yourself permission to bring more gratitude into your life today. Start now.

What are you feeling grateful for right now, and why?

22

Permission to feel excited

"Fear is excitement without breath."

Robert Heller

When the COVID pandemic first hit the UK in the spring of 2020 it caused a tsunami of difficult emotions: fear, uncertainty, panic, shock, denial, anger, grief. You name it – we were feeling it. Hidden amongst these more negative emotions, a few people were experiencing something quite different, something more enjoyable: *excitement.*

Over the months and years that have followed, I've supported many doctors who felt guilty about the positive emotions they experienced at that time. This is something we see healthcare professionals wrestle with all the time in their working lives. How do you square up the fact that you enjoy doing a job that relies on the suffering of others?

Many of us know instinctively that there's a fine line between pain and joy for humans. We enjoy watching tragic plays, reading violent novels or riding white-knuckle roller coaster rides. We're fundamentally drawn to dramatic and painful stimuli in all its forms. Nowhere is this more evident, and more normalised, than in healthcare settings.

The natural human curiosity, kindness, and compassion of healthcare professionals also draws them to those who are suffering and in pain. This can be motivated as much by our desire to help others, as by an equally normal human response: excitement in the face of adversity.

As a working psychiatrist and therapist, I feel great professional satisfaction when a patient shows me the true depth of their pain and suffering. When they feel safe enough to break down and cry, or show me their raw vulnerability in some other way, I feel pride for doing my job well. I've provided an environment safe enough for them to begin to heal and this makes me feel good. But at the same time, I can feel potent feelings of distress from empathising with their pain, and pangs of guilt for feeling positive emotions in the face of it.

This is much like the feelings I get when lancing a boil – a process that can be both painful and satisfying in equal measure. There is, after all, a reason that the YouTube phenomenon Dr Pimple Popper exists![15] (Warning: if you enjoy watching people squeeze spots or lance boils, this channel can be highly addictive. It can also bring on all the mixed emotional experiences I'm talking about here.)

When you look at these moments of conflicting

emotions more closely and honestly, you may notice that it isn't simply the prospect of healing something that brings relief. There's also something inherently pleasurable about the intensity of the suffering endured to get to that point. This may sound a bit sadistic at first – we can all be a little sadistic at times – but let's remember this is a very common everyday human experience. It's instinctive to 'want to look', however nervously, when something bad is about to happen. It's the feeling you get when you drive past an accident at the side of the road and you can't help but turn your head to see what's happened.

The doctors who experienced being 'in the right place at the right time' during the COVID pandemic often found the excitement they felt amongst the suffering of others deeply uncomfortable. The emotional high that came from being able to positively impact the outcome of a painful situation often left them feeling guilty, or more potently, ashamed. They began to think that there was something deeply wrong with them when, in fact, they were just experiencing a normal human response.

The buzz we get in the face of adversity is a common everyday experience in the world of a healthcare professional. It's the buzz a GP gets when they pick up a rare and potentially fatal condition in a patient. It's the pleasure an intensive care clinician gets from saving the life of a critically ill patient. It's the satisfaction I get from releasing this book into the world, knowing that there is a doctor out there somewhere suffering who might benefit from reading it.

The positive emotions we feel in the face of suffering are as normal and healthy as the discomfort we feel. Excitement and suffering are the light and the shadow of our human experiences. Give yourself permission to feel the joy and the pain of these experiences without judging them as good or bad. All our human emotions are important and they need to be validated, and felt, to lead a joyful life.

23

Permission to feel joy

"Joy is supposed to slither through the cracks of your imperfect life."

From *Joy Chose You* by Donna Ashworth

On the Joyful Doctor Podcast, I start each episode by asking my guests what it means to them to be joyful. Each guest's answer is unique and reinforces my theory that, despite many great attempts to define it, joy means different things to different people.

Many people experience joy as a short-lived feeling of intense pleasure or a mindful appreciation of the moment, and many dictionary definitions and emotion researchers would agree with this. Others describe joy as a quieter, more peaceful, deeper sense of connection to something meaningful, akin to contentment or happiness.

I don't feel the need to pin joy down to a single definition. What's more interesting to me, is what joy means to each of us as individuals, and what it means to us collectively as human beings living in communities and as a species on this planet.

For me personally, being joyful means experiencing *all* of life's rich tapestry of emotions. A joyful life is one full of love and loss, relief and pain, contentment and despair. For me, living joyfully means to live wholeheartedly, trying to embrace all of life's moments with curiosity, compassion and loving acceptance. It means failing and falling, as well as succeeding and soaring.

When I think about my experiences of joy in connection with others, I think about shared moments of deep connection and fulfilment, shared humanity and suffering, of comfort and love. I think about the six shared values that my team at The Joyful Doctor embody in their work every day – compassion, connection, gratitude, acceptance, choices and, above all else, *permission*.

What does joy mean to you?

How do you experience joy in your life?

How can you give yourself permission to feel joyful today?

24

Permission to be you

"Be yourself; everyone else is already taken."
Oscar Wilde

At the age of five I declared to my mum that I wanted to be a doctor. Since that day, it's often felt like my whole life has been about that pursuit. Even now, nearly forty years later, with a generally healthy perspective on life, I'm yet to fully disentangle medicine from my sense of self. I need to continually remind myself that I am *more than a doctor*.

As a psychiatrist and a therapist specialising in the mental health of doctors, I'm reminded daily that the study and practice of medicine can be dangerous. It can mess with your head and, if you're not careful, it can even cost you your life.

Of course, there's nothing wrong with feeling the significance and privilege of your chosen work. As a doctor, to know that you've helped another human being to feel less pain is a wonderful thing. It's just vitally important that we give ourselves permission to be our *whole* selves, not just a narrow version of ourselves, defined by our work or our other roles in life.

We are more than just doctors. We are more than just children, parents, siblings, lovers, friends. More than our work or our roles in the wider community. More than our hobbies, interests and pursuits. We are gloriously unique and complex human beings.

To live our fullest, most joyful, most authentic lives we must give ourselves permission to feel *all* of our feelings – the wonderful, joyful, uplifting ones and the sticky, icky, miserable ones. We must give ourselves permission to need what we need and love what we love. Permission to be ill, to fall apart and rise again, to be vulnerable, courageous and proud.

In short, we must give ourselves, and each other, the permission to be who we truly are.

Give yourself the most precious gift on earth – the permission to be you.

Note to self: '*More than a doctor*' – good title for another book?

Where to get help

Please seek help

if you need to
when you need to
before you need to

—

Resources

The resources on the following pages are separated into 'doctor-specific' and 'general' resources for all.
They are primarily UK-based.
Many have useful information available to all, and some signpost resources in other countries around the world.

—

Joyful Doctor Community

If you are a doctor, please join us at:
www.joyfuldoctor.com/join-us

Doctor-Specific Resources

The Joyful Doctor
www.joyfuldoctor.com

NHS Practitioner Health
www.practitionerhealth.nhs.uk

Doctors in Distress
www.doctors-in-distress.org.uk

Financial Support for Doctors
www.doctorshelp.org.uk

British Doctors and Dentists Group
(Addiction Support)
www.bddg.org

Doctors' Support Network
www.dsn.org.uk

You Okay, Doc?
www.youokaydoc.org.uk

Permission to Thrive
www.shapestoolkit.com/permission-to-thrive

General Resources

SHOUT Text Support Line
www.giveusashout.org
Text SHOUT to 85258

The Samaritans
www.samaritans.org
Tel: 116 123

Switchboard (LGBTQ+)
www.switchboard.lgbt
Tel: 0800 0119 100

Alcoholics Anonymous
www.alcoholics-anonymous.org.uk
Tel: 0800 917 7650

Workaholics Anonymous
www.wa-uk.org

Beat Eating Disorders
www.beateatingdisorders.org.uk

Find a therapist at:

British Association for Behavioural & Cognitive
Psychotherapies
www.babcp.com/CBTRegister/Search

British Association for Counselling Psychotherapy
www.bacp.co.uk/search/Therapists

Thank Yous

I would like to thank the following people with all my heart

My readers:

You

The loving families of:

Rose Polge, Daksha Emson and Freya Emson

Two colleagues who helped save my life:

Andrew Broadley & Thirza Pieters

My 'book buddy':

Shivanthi Sathanandan

My incredible editors:

Jo Kirkcaldy, Maggie Gould, Julia Powell

My cover designer:

Alexandra Roberts

My cover quote champions:

Adam Kay, Clare Gerada, Helen Garr

My proofreader:

Steve Collier

My work supporters:

My incredible team at The Joyful Doctor AKA Team Joy
In particular

The 'Joyful Storytellers':
Maddy Du Mont, Sarah Goulding, Katya Miles
Angela Qureshi, Julie Mitchell

My 'back end' support team:
Brad Walker & Olga Cherkasova

My constant cheerleaders:
Julia Baxendine-Jones
Sheela Hobden, Michelle Gooding
Rachel Milne, Emily Fulleylove

And all those who sat with me online as I wrote this book

All the staff at NHS Practitioner Health:
In particular
Kate Little, Lee David, Richard Jones, Lucy Warner

My Permission to Thrive co-pilot:
Rachel Morris

My friends and family:

My husband Chris & my children Leo and Emily
My parents 'Ma and Pa' & my brothers Tom and Brad
My 'mum friends' Julie and Helen
The Greencraig Massive
'My Lovely' Katrin Wilson & 'Mate' Karen Dunstan

My fellow recovering addicts around the world:

Anonymous and otherwise

**The many therapists and healthcare professionals
who have helped me over the years:**

In particular
Pat King, Peter Bryan, Verity Spencer

My Kickstarter campaign supporters:

A special thank you to all those wonderful souls who supported
my fundraising campaign in January 2020, so I could keep
The Joyful Doctor running while I started this book.

You helped me believe it was possible.

Special mention to:
Catherine Cosgrove
Rachel Crowder
Claire Thomas

Thank You

Notes on Sources

1. Gerada C, Sidhu A, Griffiths F. Doctors and suicide. BMJ. 2024;386:q1758.

2. Zimmermann C, Strohmaier S, Herkner H, Niederkrotenthaler T, Schernhammer E. Suicide rates among physicians compared with the general population in studies from 20 countries: gender stratified systematic review and meta-analysis. BMJ. 2024;386:e078964.

3. United Kingdom. Office for National Statistics. Suicide by healthcare related occupations, England, 2011 to 2015 and 2016 to 2020 registrations. 2021. No:13768.

4. Doctors in Distress. National Suicide Memorial Day for Health and Care Workers [Internet]. 2024 [cited 2024 Sep 3]. Available from: www.doctors-in-distress.org.uk /national-memorial-day

5. Parsa-Parsi RW. The revised Declaration of Geneva: a modern-day physician's pledge. JAMA. 2017;318(20): 1971-1972.

6. Equality Act 2010. [cited 2024 Sep 3]. Available from: www.legislation.gov.uk/ukpga/2010/15/contents

7. National Autistic Society. Autistic women and girls [Internet]. 2024 [cited 2024 Sep 3]. Available from: www.autism.org.uk/advice-and-guidance/what-is-autism/autistic-women-and-girls

8. Shaw SCK, Fossi A, Carravallah LA, et al. The experiences of autistic doctors: a cross-sectional study. Front Psychiatry. 2023;14:1160994

9. Joyce L. Report of an independent inquiry into the care and treatment of Daksha Emson MBBS, MRCPsych, MSc and her daughter Freya. North East London Strategic Health Authority; 2003.

10. Project Semicolon. [Internet]. 2023 [cited 2024 Sep 3]. Available from: www.projectsemicolon.com

11. Brown B. The Power of Vulnerability. [Online Video] TEDxHouston.2010. www.ted.com/talks/brene_brown _the_power_of_vulnerability

12. Ziegler S, Bednasch K, Baldofski S, et al. Long durations from symptom onset to diagnosis and from diagnosis to treatment in obsessive-compulsive disorder; A retrospective self-report study. PloS One. 2021;16(12): e0261169.

13. Salkovskis PM. Understanding and treating obsessive-compulsive disorder. Behav Res Ther. 1999;37:S29-S52.

14. Brown B. Dare to lead. London: Vermilion; 2018.

15. Dr. Pimple Popper. Home [YouTube Channel]. 2024 [cited 2024 Sep 3] Available from: www.youtube.com/ channel/UCgrsF4TYwmrV0QsXb8 AoeHQ

Spread Permission

If you have enjoyed this book,
or found it helpful in any way,
please leave a review on Amazon

About the Author

Dr Caroline Walker is a Doctors' Wellbeing Specialist who lives with her family in Kent. She works as a psychiatrist and therapist for NHS Practitioner Health. In 2017 she founded The Joyful Doctor – an organisation dedicated to improving the wellbeing of doctors and other caring professionals.

Caroline is an international role-model for doctors living with mental and physical health conditions.

She has recently given herself permission
to call herself an author.

Permission is her first book.

Website: www.joyfuldoctor.com
Email (general): teamjoy@joyfuldoctor.com
Email (books): books@joyfuldoctor.com
Facebook: @joyfuldoctor
Twitter/X: @joyful_doctor
Instagram: thejoyfuldoctor
LinkedIn: The Joyful Doctor

Printed in Great Britain
by Amazon

54633527R00126